HOW TO BE A CANCER MAVERICK

MAVERICK

by Nina Joy

First published in 2015 by
The Solopreneur Publishing Company Ltd
Cedars Business Centre, Barnsley Road, Hemsworth, West Yorkshire WF9 4PU
www.thesolopreneur.co.uk

The publisher makes no representation, expressed or implied, with regards to the accuracy of the information contained in this book, and cannot accept any responsibility or liability.

ISBN 978-0-9927840-6-5

Printed in the U.K.

MEDICAL DISCLAIMER

Cancer is a very serious and individual disease. It is not my aim to provide advice about treatments for cancer or any other disease, and any associated symptoms. I recommend people seek specialist medical advice. The information provided in this book is not intended, or implied, to be a substitute for professional medical advice, nor is it intended to be for diagnosis or treatment. I simply want to share what I have learned, and give details of the things I have done that have worked for me, to stay well against all the odds.

Please note: All web-links, and contact details, throughout this book, were correct at the time of going to press.

As a society, we seem too ready to accept the hold that cancer has over us. It sometimes feels like there's an epidemic as it affects so many families. Cancer Research UK tells us that our lifetime risk of getting cancer is 1 in 3. This is expected to rise to 1 in 2 by 2020!

Doesn't this tell us that in 21st century living, we are doing something wrong?

Maybe you have already been touched by cancer, which is why you are reading this book. Perhaps you want to take steps to live a healthier and longer life. This book will also give ideas for your own personal healing or wellness plan.

CONTACT NINA

www.ninajoy.com

Twitter @ninajoy1

Facebook – How to be a Cancer Maverick, Ninajoyspeaker, The Cancer Mavericks

CHARITY DONATION

 A donation from the sale of each book will be given to YES TO LIFE

'YES TO LIFE' - HELPING TO MAKE INTEGRATIVE MEDICINE AVAILABLE TO EVERYONE IN THE UK

'Yes to Life' is inspired by a vision of a different way of responding to cancer. Their aim is to change culture and attitude and to make integrative cancer care, an approach which utilises and combines the best of both orthodox and Complementary & Alternative Medicine ('CAM'), readily available throughout the UK. They are a unique organisation and the only UK charity directly supporting people with cancer in taking an integrative approach to their care.

Dedications

I dedicate this book to the 3 women who bring a serious amount of girl power into my life...

My sister Julie, who is my rock even when everything else in the world is like shifting sand.

My niece Lucie, you make me laugh, you're my conscience when I need to be blogging more, and you push me to achieve more than I think I can.

Wendy, for being my friend through thick and thin, since perms were in fashion, and being the best holiday buddy a girl could have.

Testimonial

The person who wrote this wanted to remain anonymous because of work commitments, but gave her blessing for me to use her words. Thank you 'T' - it makes all my work and campaigning for people to see that there are choices and hope when all seems hopeless, worthwhile. Fortunately, I receive many words of kindness similar to the one below, but without doubt this is one of my favourites. Nina Joy.

Dear Nina,

I just wanted to share a bit of news with. Firstly, I want you to understand that when I heard I had a recurrence of cancer in February I read your book 'The Adventures of a Cancer Maverick'. I was so inspired by your story and it filled me with so much hope even though I was told that my cancer was inoperable and chemo would be only palliative.

8 weeks ago I began an alternative protocol after consulting with Patricia Peat. Because of the energy, hope and practical ideas that your follow up book 'How to Be a Cancer Maverick', and some of the othercancerucan community filled me with, I felt energised and empowered to really go for it.

I just wanted to let you know that I've just been to the hospital this afternoon. The tumour has shrunk from

23mm to 15mm in 8 weeks, and my blood test has dropped from nearly 300 to 66! The oncologist and nurse said they couldn't explain or understand what had happened and appeared quite perplexed! We were absolutely delighted!

I want you to know that you are doing a terrific job in helping people to make a real difference to their health and that I am so very grateful to you for helping me to see a path I could follow and believe in. I know there's lots of work still to be done but this is so much more than I could have hoped for.

Thank you so very much. God bless you. Love T xxx

Online Book Store

Available from

www.oodlebooks.com and Amazon

both in print and on Kindle.

Acknowledgements

- The team at the 3E Centre for your knowledge, expertise and care. Thank you for teaching me all you know, and helping me to believe.
- 'Yes to Life' who do a great job in the promotion of integrative medicine. Because of you I found 'Cancer Options'. Because of you I am still around to write this book.
- Patricia and Hayley of Cancer Options who I think of as my cancer IFA. Your knowledge and dedication are phenomenal. Thank you for helping me navigate and enjoy this adventure.
- Team Nina – all my friends, family, fellow Mavericks, and virtual supporters through my blog, speaking, and social media. Thank you for your support and confidence in me – together we are amazing!
- And finally, a very big thank you to Gail Powell, my publisher, who has cajoled and supported me to get the book which was swirling around in my head into print, which is yet another big tick for my Bucket List.

FOREWORD
by Dr Julie Coffey, G.P.

When it comes to cancer most people regard what their doctor says as the truth, the whole truth, and nothing but the truth. When they're told they are probably going to die soon, they invariably do. Had Nina accepted this 'truth' over two years ago, I doubt she'd be around today writing this book. She was given a terrible prognosis when she was diagnosed, and the way the cancer took hold of her body I have little doubt she would have succumbed, had she not questioned the 'truth'.

I love Nina's comparison of a conventional medical doctor to a financial advisor tied to one bank. That financial advisor can't advise about outside products or services, they might not even know about them at all. I've been a doctor for 20 years working in the NHS, but not really thought of it like that. How often do we doctors give advice on treatments we can't provide – just about never is the general rule of thumb. Worse than that though – anything vaguely alternative and not medicine-based is often scorned and labelled quackery.

Some time ago I read 'A Cancer Therapy' by Dr Max Gerson. The book documents 50 cases of advanced cancer, cured by diet. You might be wondering why you haven't heard of this book, surely it was a best seller? When I came across it I was flabbergasted at the publication date – 1958! I wondered how I'd got through medical school, and 20 years as a doctor without hearing about it. I wondered why my colleagues looked at me as if I'd lost it when I tried to talk about curing cancer with diet.

Medicine is called medicine, because doctors treat people with medicine. Doctors are experts on what can go wrong with the body, and what medicine to use to try and fix the problem. Doctors are generally not experts on health, we weren't taught about that, only illness. Doctors don't generally look at the whole person, their whole body. If you have cancer – they look at the cancer. There is little discussion about what went wrong to allow this cancer to happen in the first place. This is flawed because even if the cancer can be cut out, isn't the cause still there? If your body has made cancer once isn't it going to do it again if you don't do anything different?

Sometimes medicine comes in the form of chemotherapy. Chemotherapy is basically poison, there are no two ways about that. The idea is to kill the cancer before you kill the patient. It's very crude and it steam-rollers over the very thing you need to keep cancer at bay – your immune system. But if you've already had chemotherapy – there is still so much you can do to rebuild your immune system.

The work of Dr Gerson has been refined and built on in the decades since his book was published. What you have in your hands now is an up to date encapsulation of that work. It's a straight forward easy read, but the information is very powerful, it could save your life.

I imagine Nina's doctors are really pleased that she's doing so well, but I wouldn't be surprised that they're a bit annoyed on some level too! She is a Maverick, she hasn't done what she's been told to, she hasn't accepted anything the 'experts' have said without questioning and researching herself. And ultimately she's proved them wrong.

Nina takes you through the important areas to nurture yourself back to health. The most important one of all is straightening out your mindset. I think most people close down with fear when given the dreaded cancer diagnosis, this is not going to help you.

It's not just a matter of skipping to the 'doing' bits of the book; like what to eat, you have to 'become' that healthy, well, and positive person in your mind first. I have seen many people make themselves ill, or make themselves more ill, by having a negative and worrying mindset. Don't underestimate how important this is, it is vital. Nina explains how to straighten this out.

Nina goes onto explain how to put less toxins into your body, and how to facilitate removing them. This further encourages healing within your body. The body has remarkable healing power, providing it is given what it needs. Our bodies are built out of what we feed them. If you have cancer your body needs the right and best stuff. It does not need the stuff that will fuel cancer further.

Nina also explains the value of alternative therapies, the sort of stuff that most doctors really do turn their nose up at. These can play a valuable role in my opinion.

This book isn't about alienating your doctor. It's about listening to what they say, but not taking it as gospel. This book puts a lot of knowledge in your hands, written by a person who is probably enjoying the best health she's had in years (despite having cancer). Knowledge can be very powerful indeed, if you use it.
This is a book filled with positivity. With information like this there is no need to roll over and give up, even if you have cancer. If you do what Nina has done – accept your current predicament, and see it as a massive wake up call, perhaps you can annoy your doctors too by tearing up their wholly inaccurate prognosis.

The one piece of advice I can personally give you, as a doctor, is not to be put off exploring the information in this book if, or when, you come up against resistance from your own doctor.

Dr. Julie Coffey
G.P. and author

CONTENT

CHAPTER 1 – MY STORY

What do you do when you find out you have cancer?

This happened to me in August 2012 when I found out that I had breast cancer which had spread to my lymph nodes. Further scans showed that the cancer had already spread to my lungs, liver, and bones.

In medical speak -
Diagnosis:
Aug 2012 Locally advanced right breast cancer, ductal carcinoma Grade3, ER positive 8/8, PR positive 4/8, HER2 negative. Staging CT scan with sternal metastasis, small lung nodules and single liver lesion.

In the blink of an eye, your life changes beyond comprehension. Everything you have held dear, and have taken for granted, is blown into smithereens. The future you thought you had – gone. The events and experiences you thought were yet to come – gone. Have you had your last birthday, your last Christmas? And bizarrely, I wondered if I would get to see the next series of Downton Abbey.

Welcome to, what was for me, the unfamiliar world of medical jargon and hospital procedures.

My prognosis was pretty dire – again, here is the medical speak:

> *Whereas exact prognosis in the individual patient is impossible to predict, we have data from a local study using the Cancer Registry showing that patients who are diagnosed with metastatic disease at first presentation have worse prognosis than patients who are originally treated for early breast cancer and then develop metastatic disease. Patients diagnosed with metastatic disease have median overall survival of 3.6 months from our Leeds data. This means that half of the patients will die of their disease within 3.6 months whereas half will live longer. The range of survival is between 3 and 54 months.*

When your life expectancy is expressed in months, you know that you are in real trouble. I decided that I really didn't like words ending in *osis*.

I am now well over 2 years on from that diagnosis. I have learned so much in that time – about myself, about other people, about cancer – its causes and treatments.

It hasn't all been plain sailing though. By March 2013, 7 months after diagnosis, I was not in a good place.

My breast tumour was growing, and was about to ulcerate through the skin. It was coming out through my nipple and the smell was horrendous and nauseating. The tumour under my right arm, in the lymph, was growing. It was like a large hard-boiled egg, meaning that I couldn't put my arm down close to my body. It was also difficult to raise my arm and I had really restricted movement. Making the bed, or lifting the lid of the big wheely bin, were challenges I found hard to manage, yet I had to as there was no-one here to do it for me. I had fluid on my lungs which made a strange bubbly sound when I breathed in and out. Breathing was difficult which meant that walking more than a few steps was hard work. I couldn't breathe if I laid down to sleep, so had to be propped up, plus I couldn't lay on my painful right side. I also had a lot of pain from my sternum meaning that I certainly couldn't lay on my front, and even on my back it was incredibly painful – I felt as though I had an elephant on my chest. Not a good place to keep one.

I remember my birthday that year, on March 16th 2013. I was due to go into Leeds to meet my friends Rita and Sue, to have lunch and go on the Leeds Eye big wheel. I really wanted to go, but wasn't sure I could manage it. My niece, Lucie, came to the rescue and accompanied me. I really needed to lean on her as I was very slowly walking through town. I had an annoying persistent cough. We went for lunch as you do on your birthday – but I didn't have any appetite at all, so I ordered a smoothie. I couldn't even manage to get that down.

I did get on Leeds Eye though, but despite my big teddy bear furry coat I was frozen. I'm not sure that I realised just how frail I was at that point, but I did feel that I was fading. Lucie, and my sister Julie, have only recently told me how worried they were about me at that time, and that they thought I would not last very long. However, as those of you who are familiar with my first book 'The Adventures of a Cancer Maverick'*, I had another cunning plan and pursued another avenue of treatment which was amazingly successful. I tell you this because it's important to know that cancer is a roller-coaster. And that even if your condition has deteriorated, you can come back from it.

You may be wondering how I am now, 2 ½ years after diagnosis. Amazingly, given the information above, I am really well. I look and feel healthy, I'm not in any pain at all, and I am living my life to the absolute max! Writing this, my second book, building my speaking business, taking lots of holidays, and having more fun than you can shake a stick at. Plus, of course, taking good care of myself. I can't become complacent and take my health for granted now can I?

The cancer is still there in my breast, if I have a good old grope I can feel it, but it seems to be having a bit of a snooze, as do the other tumours. My blood tests show my CEA tumour markers at less than one! (This is good, the lower the better). Although scans had previously shown cancer in my spine and pelvis, my last bone scan couldn't find a trace with only a bit in my sternum, which is the breast bone (not surprising for breast cancer I suppose). At my routine check-up in September 2014, I asked the doctor if I was in remission. He agreed that yes this was a reasonable description of my condition. Wow! And wow again. I secretly always thought that I wasn't destined to hear that word, even though I hoped I would. Result!

This scenario was not seen as a possibility in 2012. It was expected that I would experience a downward spiral into illness, and that I would die, probably quite soon. So what happened to change this seemingly inevitable course of action?

The answer to that is that I have done many things. Cancer is a complex disease, and I believe that it needs to be treated on many levels to achieve healing and wellness. It has taken me a great deal of time and money to get to the position I am in today. Not everyone has the time, or freedom, or resources, to do what I did.

Which is why I want to share what I have learned. That is why I blogged throughout about what I was discovering and experiencing at www.ninajoy.com. That is why I wrote my first book "The Adventures of a Cancer Maverick"*. It gives a blow by blow account from the day I found there was a change in my right breast through all the amazing treatments I had in order to get well during 2012 and 2013. I have had lots of lovely reviews on my book which gives me a great deal of pride and satisfaction. I have also had many messages telling me that my story has given hope and inspiration to people facing a cancer diagnosis, which is just fantastic.

However, I am contacted almost daily by people looking for detailed advice and guidance from me on how to cope with a cancer diagnosis, on what can be done when the doctors say "there is nothing more we can do". There seems to be a real need and thirst for knowledge, yet people don't know where to turn, especially when the conventional medicine door shuts.

The reason I am writing this book is to provide the answers, in detail, to the questions I'm asked time after time. To give you tried and tested, practical strategies for dealing with a cancer diagnosis.

I also believe that these strategies are very powerful preventative measures to protect your future health. Prevention is much less of a challenge than curing what I've got!

I am not suggesting that you should do exactly what I have done, as only you can know what resonates for you, but I do hope that it will give you some ideas and signposts to your own healing and wellness, regardless of whether you have been diagnosed with cancer.

It has been said that what has happened to me is nothing short of a miracle. It feels like it to me! But the good news is that this miracle didn't just land on me from heaven. It's one which I have had to figure out and work for, which makes it all the sweeter. More importantly it means that I can share the steps that I have taken, so that you may be able to create your own miracle too.

Right then, hang on to your hats, let's go *Maverick*!

*Adventures of a Cancer Maverick is available to purchase at www.oodlebooks.com

CHAPTER 2– THE DREADED OSIS WORDS – DIAGNOSIS AND PROGNOSIS

There are some moments in life which you remember very clearly, no matter how much time passes. The day I received my diagnosis was one of those. It was a Thursday, late afternoon. My sister Julie was with me for moral support. The reason for the appointment was to find out my specific treatment plan for breast cancer, to achieve a cure – it was likely to be chemo, mastectomy, reconstruction, radiotherapy, and then 5 years of hormone therapy. Hardly a walk in the park, but leading eventually to a cure.

That isn't how it panned out. Not at all. Instead of discussing my curative plan, I was told that the cancer had spread – to my lymph, lungs, liver and bones. That seemed a very long list. All I could think was "oh my God! I'm riddled with it!" And then the fateful words. *"This means that we are no longer looking at a cure."*

I felt as though my heart stopped. Maybe it did. Outwardly I remained very calm and asked what that meant. It meant that the treatment plan changed. Much of the previous plan was to stop the spread of cancer, but clearly that ship had sailed.

The treatment now proposed was systemic chemotherapy (which means that it goes throughout the whole body). The idea was that the chemo would halt or shrink the tumours to buy me some more time. I would be monitored every three months, and when the tumours started to grow again, which they would, then more chemo would be administered. And so on. Until it didn't work anymore. I asked about other options. Apparently there were none.

I now know that to be absolutely untrue. But I didn't then.

The doctors were pressing me to urgently proceed with the chemo, as this was the only treatment they had available, and due to the seriousness of the disease, time was of the essence. So much so, that it was at the same appointment when I was told that I was "incurable", that I was asked to sign the chemo consent form. I'm surprised I could even sign my own name after that bombshell! But I did.

The letter came through to say that my appointment for chemo pre-assessment would be on the 4th October 2012.

So what do you do when you're told those fateful words "you've got cancer". It feels as though your whole world has fallen apart. You wonder if you're going to die. In my case it seemed that I would, and maybe quite soon. This is an incredibly difficult time, for you, and also for your family and friends.

Even so, I believe that the quicker you can come to terms with your diagnosis, the better. After all, it's a reality that you cannot change at this point in time. So better to accept it. I don't mean to resign yourself to the outcome, merely to accept the current reality. This then frees up your energy to get on with your plan of action. Having said that, it's no mean feat to accept such bad news.

Here is how I did it -

What to do when you're initially diagnosed:-

- Hit the 'pause button'. Take time out for yourself, clear your diary as much as you possibly can and cut yourself some slack. This is huge news, so don't worry about work or your 'To Do' list for once. This has to come first. You need this time to process the enormity of the information and how you feel about it.
- Journalling worked really well for me at this point. There is something therapeutic about getting hold of a pen and paper and writing down how you are feeling - the good, the bad, what you're afraid of, what your hopes are, in fact anything and everything that is going through your head. You can do this at the beginning or end of the day, or both, whatever works for you. It can be helpful to look back and re-read as the days and weeks go by, and see what progress you are making. What a great excuse

to buy yourself a lovely new notebook. . I have created a fabulous journal to go with this book. To purchase a copy go to – www.oodlebooks.com Or if you prefer a keyboard, you could blog, like I did at ninajoy.com – to be shared with others only if you wish to do so

- Find someone you can talk to, really talk to. Honestly. This isn't always your nearest and dearest, as you try to protect them – remember that they are going through this too. It might be an acquaintance who isn't quite so emotionally involved, or even a stranger, for example a healthcare professional. Don't bottle everything up – by expressing and talking it through you will reach a stage where you can accept what is happening to you more quickly.
- Allow yourself to feel sad. It's a bit like a bereavement. You've lost the health and maybe even the future you wanted for yourself. Acknowledge those feelings, you are allowed to feel sad, although it's not helpful to stay there for too long.
- Be as kind to yourself as you would be to your child, if she or he were ill. We don't tend to give the same level of compassion and care to ourselves as we would to others. We can almost blame ourselves for getting cancer – especially if there are any lifestyle factors involved, and feel more inclined to punish ourselves rather than nurture. You must be your own best friend - you need to get used to the idea of self-care as you will be doing a lot more of it in the months and years to come. Make sure that you

have good food, prepared with love and care, and plenty of sleep. Shock and grief is pretty tiring so you will need it. Plan some nice treats in amongst the soul searching – punishment is out, pleasure is in. That is an order!

- So, it's official. You've got cancer. Nothing and no-one can change that piece of information. Once you can absorb and accept this information, you can move on to the next phase. I know some people struggle with the question "Why me?" I didn't – because I absolutely refuse to waste energy on the things I cannot change. And once you get your diagnosis it's a bit of a done deal really isn't it? Accepting your new reality is important, because it releases your energy so that you can use it on the multitude of things which you can influence and change. Acceptance is key to moving on. Please note, that by accepting the fact you have cancer, I don't mean that you should resign yourself to accepting the prognosis as that is an entirely different matter. More of that later.

The next thing you need to do is to work on your state of mind. You might think it's too early to do that as you need to get on with your chemo, and surgery, and you will work on your spirits afterwards. But it isn't too early. It's your absolute priority right now. You will deal with every single aspect of your diagnosis, treatment and recovery, if you are in a more positive frame of mind. Just after your diagnosis, you cannot possibly be where you need to be. You have to make a conscious choice to be more positive, and then do the work.

The single most important thing you have in your armoury to deal with this situation is the power of your mind and spirit.

YOU MUST, MUST, MUST, WORK ON THIS FIRST. BEFORE DOING ANYTHING. Did I mention you must work on this first? I don't want to be too subtle about it. This is <u>not</u> an optional step. It's the one which will make the biggest difference to you, and the outcome.

My personal belief has always been that you get better results when coming from a positive angle. To supplement this I have done lots of research and reading on this over the years. What I found excited me so much, especially when I first started out as a professional speaker, that this was my chosen topic - Positivity, and the difference it makes in life and in business. Or you might prefer to call it *happiness*.

Some of the things I found out blew my mind. Let me share some of them with you.

A couple of facts for you to conjure with (source – actionforhappiness.org)

1. Most people think that if they become successful, then they'll be happy. But recent discoveries in psychology and neuroscience show that this formula is backward: happiness fuels success, not the other way around. When we're positive, our brains are more motivated, engaged, creative, energetic, resilient, and productive.

2. Positive emotions - like joy, interest, pride and gratitude - don't just feel good in the moment - they also affect our long term well-being. Research shows that experiencing positive emotions in a 3-to-1 ratio to negative ones leads to a tipping point beyond which we naturally become more resilient to adversity and better able to achieve things. The evidence linking an upbeat outlook to increased longevity is actually stronger than the evidence linking obesity to reduced longevity.

Let's just consider what this means for us in a cancer diagnosis situation –

'When we are positive our brains are more motivated, engaged, creative, energetic, resilient and productive.'

Isn't this the state you would like to be in when researching, considering, and deciding your treatment plan; especially when it comes to exactly 'how' you are going to engage with all the steps necessary, that could help you to save your own life?

If you have 3 positive emotions for every negative one, we become more resilient to *adversity* and better able to achieve things. Well, a cancer diagnosis is adversity, and being more resilient and able to achieve success, is a must if you're going to get through this. Right?

I decided that for me, it was a *must* to be in a positive mental space.

It doesn't come easily at a time like this. Firstly you have to make a conscious choice to be positive, to be happy.

My prognosis was awful. But I figured, if I only have 3 months left, I wanted them to be happy ones. And if I have 13 months, or 3 years, or 13 years, then I definitely don't want to be miserable for that long! Ultimately, I see being happy as a choice. I could have cancer, and wallow in sadness and fear, and see what that did for me mentally and physically. Or, have cancer and despite that still choose to be happy. I choose the latter.

Once you have made that decision, you have to work at it. Make no mistake, it is work – you are not going to wake up full of the joys of spring after your diagnosis –

you do have to work at it. But what better to work on than that?

I was in an ideal position to do so. I was naturally, infuriatingly, positive (apparently), and having researched and studied positivity, I knew many techniques which have been scientifically proven to have a positive impact on your state of mind. So I already knew what to work on. Lucky huh?

The first thing that I did, to help me see some light when I was in a very sad dark place, was to think about what I was grateful for. There were two reasons for this. Firstly, it is one of the scientifically proven techniques (see - actionforhappiness.org for more information on this). Secondly, and more importantly, it was because of my mum. My mum had sadly died in November 2011. She had had multiple sclerosis for many years. After my diagnosis, I remember thinking back to how she had coped with her own diagnosis. She told me that she was glad it was happening to her, and not to me or my sister Julie. That gave her a great deal of comfort, I think.

Only now did I absolutely understand how she felt. I too was glad that it was happening to me, and not to my sister. And even more so, that it wasn't happening to my niece Lucie. That would have been unbearable. This, whilst not what I would have wished for myself, was infinitely preferable to that. Once you have found that first thing to be grateful for, it gives you a little chink of light that you can build on.

Gratitude Journal

It's a good idea to write these things down, as it gives you a reminder to look back on when you need a boost.

You could write down 3 things at the end of every day that you're grateful for.

Or as I prefer to do, I write down as many things as I can possibly think of, both big and small. Set a timer for 3 minutes and write down every single thing you can think of that you're grateful for. Just keep going, no matter what. You may find that there are some surprises there, which gives you a new found appreciation for some of the people and things in your life.

I guarantee that doing this will make you feel better.

What a great excuse to treat yourself to a new notebook, or Journal (for a copy of my 'Nina Joy Journal' see link at the end of the book).

The next step for me was to build my belief. Conventional wisdom said that I would have to have chemotherapy;

that I would never get better, and my life expectancy was between 3 and 12 months. If I was lucky. When the expert in a white coat and stethoscope tells you that, you tend to believe that they know what they're talking about. Because of course they do. They have seen hundreds, thousands even, of patients and they know what the probabilities are. They have seen it all before. It feels like the end of the world. Especially, when like me you are told "it's incurable". Where do you go with that? When there is no hope.

The point is that there is hope!

This is why.

They don't know YOU.

You are the expert in you.

They don't know -
- how mentally strong you are
- how much responsibility you will take for your own health and wellness
- ...or what you are prepared to do to get well.

I was not interested in *probabilities* at all. I wanted to know what the possibilities were.

If just one person had ever survived longer, or even been cured, then I could allow myself to think that if they had done it, then maybe I could too.

Belief and Hope

One of the things which helped me to believe was to read success stories of others who were cancer survivors and thrivers, warriors, and goddesses. I thought, if they can do it, maybe I can too? I remember borrowing a number of books from 'The Haven' (a charity which offers support to women with breast cancer), and feeling really inspired by what others had achieved. There were also forums and groups that I could join and hear from people who had done what I wanted to achieve. I call them DIBs. Short for "Done It Befores". I found that learning from DIBs was one of the best ways to build my belief, and show me a way forward. That is one of the main reasons I wrote my first book "The Adventures of a Cancer Maverick", as a DIB, to share my story, and provide exactly that to others.

You need to hang out where survivors are hanging out – forums, Facebook groups, and local meet-ups. I have started such a group on Facebook with other DIBs called 'The Cancer Mavericks'. Maverick - because it might not be what you'd expect from people with cancer. It's a positive place where amazingly inspirational people share and discuss what they are doing to survive and thrive. Where you are amongst friends who can and do help each other. You are very welcome to join in. I also have my own page on Facebook: ninajoyspeaker which you might find interesting.

Having started to work on your state of mind, you are almost ready to get on with this cancer malarkey. Almost.

You need to have a look around for something you are going to need in the coming weeks and months. You may feel that you have lost it since you got your diagnosis, but have a really good look. It might be difficult to find. Try down the back of the sofa, under the bed, or in the bottom of your handbag.

What am I talking about?

Your sense of humour.

It's still there somewhere. Although you've got cancer, you haven't had a personality transplant. It can feel that you have forgotten how to laugh, or that you shouldn't be happy at a time like this, but actually the opposite is true. Laughter does your mind and body the world of good. It is the best medicine ever. If you are doubtful about the power of laughter to help you get well, watch one of my most favourite films ever, Patch Adams (starring the late great Robin Williams).

You are going to need your sense of humour more than ever, so be ready to see the funny side. Look out for the people and activities that make you laugh and make sure that you make time for them. If you're struggling to do this for yourself, recruit your funniest friend, or find your nearest 'Laughter Yoga Class' (yes, there really is such a thing!).

Finding out you have cancer means you are about to embark on the biggest adventure of your life, albeit one that you didn't choose.

Your life will never be the same again. But that will bring good things as well as bad. Life becomes even more precious, and you will appreciate even the smallest of things. You will meet people you wouldn't otherwise have met, and make the closest of friendships.

So let's embrace this situation. Find your best "bring it on!" attitude – as you are about to embark on the biggest and most important adventure of your entire life.

****

Whilst you are dealing with your own diagnosis, this is not happening in isolation. This is not just happening to you, but to all the people who love and care for you. Let's turn our attention to them, your family and friends, colleagues and acquaintances. This is a tricky time for them too. What happens over the coming weeks and months will make or break relationships. You will lose some friends – it seems that we all do.

But you will make some new ones.

You are going to need the support of those around you, so it's worth spending some time on this topic.

<u>How to talk to someone with Cancer?</u>
This topic was one of my most read blog posts. Many people have difficulty knowing how to talk to a friend or family member who has been diagnosed with cancer. In fact, some people head for the hills, and you just don't hear from them at all.

I have had that happen to me. I can understand why that might happen. I appreciate that we are all doing our best in a difficult situation, so I don't hold any grudges. People who do struggle initially with the news are often likely to come back at some point when the dust has settled. To avoid that happening to you I thought it a good idea to include this topic in my book.

Because I am so open about having cancer, people - strangers even - feel that they can talk to me and ask me about some of the more delicate things that they want to know about. One of the questions that I am often asked is "how do you talk to someone who has cancer".

So, let's explore this. Initially, I might have thought that wouldn't be an issue. Not for me, anyway. Surely? I mean, I am so open about all this stuff, even strangers can talk to me. But just because a stranger can, it doesn't mean that your nearest and dearest can. It's more complicated than that isn't it?

One of the things you learn very quickly after your cancer diagnosis is that this isn't just happening to you. It impacts on everyone around you too.

They are fearful for you - about the treatment you are facing, about the prognosis, and what the ultimate outcome will be.

They are also fearful for themselves - they are scared of losing you. They contemplate a life without you in it. They may be thinking about their own mortality. Scary stuff.

Against this background, I guess it's hardly surprising that communication can become a bit of a minefield.

Let me give you some examples of the sorts of things which have been said to me which shocked me at the time;

- When I was newly diagnosed – "This is really hard for me, my friend who had breast cancer faded fast and it was so sad when she recently died".
- From someone who found out I had incurable cancer "my cousin has cancer and she's terminal too". At the time, I had never referred to myself as having terminal cancer.
- After telling a professional adviser that I have incurable cancer – "Ha, ha, ha, don't worry none of

us will get out of this alive".

- I was out at a networking meeting, looking well, talking business when I bumped into someone I hadn't seen for a year or so. (Imagine her head leaning to one side with that over-sympathetic look on her face) – "how are you today? Are you in much pain?"
- On finding out that I have a life-limiting illness – "I hope that whatever is wrong with you isn't catching as I've been sitting next to you all morning".
- "How do you think I'll feel when something happens to you?"

All these things were said to me by intelligent, professional people. I dare say if any of them read this book they may wince a little because with hindsight it's easy to see what not to say. And yet, say it they did.

I think from those we can figure out some guidelines -
- Do not share horror stories about others with cancer and how badly it turned out.
- Take your cue from them – how do they refer to their diagnosis? Use the same terminology.
- Be sensitive to the surroundings and company – they may not wish to share personal information in that particular environment, so respect that.
- Don't make jokes and light of a serious situation until you are really certain it would be appropriate.
- Don't make assumptions about the symptoms they may be feeling.

- Don't just think of yourself – put yourself in their shoes and consider how you might feel if it were you.

What this tells us is that you need to be prepared. Do not wing it. Especially when your friend or family member is newly diagnosed. It's a sensitive time, and their emotions are very near the surface. So the responsibility is yours to get it right – they already have more than enough on their plate.

Here's what it is like if you did want to try and put yourself into the shoes of the person who has received the bad news.

Initially, it is a total shock, and all consuming. It occupies every single waking second. Every waking thought. There are some real physiological symptoms of shock – understanding these can make it easier to comprehend what is going on for them, the impact on the person, and therefore how to communicate.

Emotional and psychological symptoms of trauma:	
Shock, denial, or disbelief	**Confusion, difficulty concentrating**
Anger, irritability, mood swings	Anxiety and fear
Guilt, shame, self-blame	**Withdrawing from others**
Feeling sad or hopeless	Feeling disconnected or numb

Physical symptoms of trauma:	
Insomnia or nightmares	Fatigue
Being startled easily	**Difficulty concentrating**
Racing heartbeat	**Edginess and agitation**
Aches and pains	Muscle tension

Once you understand the impact of the diagnosis, you can see why you need to take responsibility as your friend, or loved one, will have enough on their plate and they will not have the emotional energy to nurse you through it too. I am not suggesting that you need to understand these challenges in detail, but it is useful to be aware of them. Not everyone is affected in the same way though, so don't assume that what I am saying is the same for everyone – it is just a guideline.

I have asked some other people with cancer how they would like to be talked to -

"I would advise them to think about what they would want a friend to say to them if they had cancer"

"You're still the same person. It's hard to talk knowing you're likely to hurt them, but you don't have the emotional energy for them too"

"Friends should just face facts, you are still you, just that you have crap to deal with, which is easier with understanding friends"

"Have a good old cry together, and then just get on with it"

"I told them I was dealing with it, it was ok for them to feel a bit awkward, but if they wanted to help then try to be normal for me. The friends who head for the hills are the ones that fear losing us most, or just think there is something THEY should be doing, but don't know what."

Here are some DO's for talking to someone with cancer.

- Get comfortable with it, if you're not it will show.
- See it as an opportunity to be a good and supportive friend.
- Make some reference to the situation – don't ignore it. It IS happening, and it IS a big deal.
- Take your cue from them – how do they talk about their diagnosis, how are they feeling?
- Really listen.
- Have some questions/statements ready so that you don't put your Size 5's in it by being off the cuff and unprepared. For example, *"I was so sorry to hear your news. How are you and your family coping?"*
- Don't say "if there's anything I can do, just ask". They have enough to think about, without allocating tasks across friends and family.
- Do something nice without having to be asked – make a healthy meal, buy a book, offer to give a lift to the hospital, bring a bunch of flowers, just DO what you feel would be nice for them.

Back to the question: "How do you talk to someone who has cancer?"

Let me give you my own personal answer to this. I would say - how did you talk to me before? If we had long serious discussions about business and the state of the economy, let's carry on doing that. If we used to talk about fashion and men and make-up and going out - let's do that.

If you were a close friend who knows all about my hopes and dreams, and fears and worries then inevitably you will need to broach the cancer thing. Because it is now a big part of my life. It has changed my life beyond recognition, and as my friend you will want to understand that. Won't you?

I'm still the same person, but I'm having a life-changing experience. I'm learning and being challenged like never ever before. But I haven't had a personality transplant. I still need to be me, not a cancer patient. Having said that, to ignore that I have cancer and to never refer to it is rather odd. Like a big elephant in the room. Sometimes, when something big has just happened (like when I found out that the cancer has spread to my spine), I would like that acknowledging. It's a big deal! Or at least it is until I come to terms with it, and decide what I'm going to do about it.

If you never ask, or never show any emotion or reaction, it seems that you don't care. And, I'd rather like to think that you do, and so will your friend or relative. It is a difficult time for everyone and you are learning how to cope as well. Hopefully all the observations and suggestions within this chapter have helped you how to be more understanding and supportive.

CHAPTER 3 – GET YOUR MAVERICK ON

Maverick (noun) –

...an unorthodox or independent-minded person

Do you remember the film Top Gun? If not, you need to watch it immediately. Tom Cruise is a Top Gun pilot, and his call name is 'Maverick'. Men want to be him. And women want to.... Well, you can imagine what women want. At the start of the film, the fact that he is maverick is portrayed as a bad thing – that he's a loose cannon and can't be relied on. But by the end of the movie, we can see why being different, and having the courage to follow your gut instincts, is the only way to achieve a different outcome.

I have always seen being maverick as a good thing – if you do what you always do, you get what you have always got. How can you keep on doing the same actions, and expect different results? If you want the same you follow a path. If you want to do something amazing, you need to go first, to blaze a trail.

To achieve something remarkable then, the world needs more mavericks.

****

The Wake-Up Call

I didn't know I was going to be a 'Cancer Maverick'. I started out as a 'Cancer Virgin'. I didn't really know anything about cancer, having been lucky enough not to have been closely affected by it. I had been pretty healthy all my life, and did not know how to be a patient. I'm not patient! It doesn't even belong in the same sentence as my name.

From being a very little girl I have always wanted to understand "why" before doing anything. If that's my way, then it certainly applies for something as serious as a life or death decision about cancer treatment. Even though I had no medical knowledge, I had my logical inquiring mind. How could I embark on that without questioning why? I couldn't. And when I did start questioning I realised that I really didn't get what I was being faced with at all.

I had a real dilemma going on in my head. I have no medical knowledge whatsoever, but intellectually I just didn't think that chemo made sense. My body was in crisis and needed care and nurturing, not poisoning. I didn't see the cancer as an invader – my body had made this thing, and I felt that it could therefore get rid of it. The immune system is amazing, but if you have chemo it wipes out the very thing you need to heal. It seemed to me that the tumours were merely a symptom and even if you could get rid of them (which wasn't a possibility for me according to the doctors), then wouldn't the root cause still be there?   Surely we needed to tackle the root cause?

Because I'd been so healthy, I didn't have any experience of alternative or complementary medicine either.   In fact, I thought all that stuff was a bit woo-woo, and you had to be a bit of a sandal-wearing, bohemian- type, to embrace all that.   So it wasn't that I was choosing the alternative over the orthodox.

Something else I didn't get.   I didn't like the language that is often used about cancer.   The "I hate cancer", and that it's a battle, or a fight.

I didn't see it that way at all.   I had my own particular view point on this – ah yes, that maverick streak is alive and well.

I thought cancer was my body's way of making me listen.   To tell me that I wasn't looking after it properly and that there had better be some big changes – and fast!

I see cancer as a massive wake-up call.   It's your body demanding some attention, telling you that all is not well, and that you need to change.   Whatever you have been doing so far has resulted in this cancer, so it's time to take a microscopic, honest look at yourself and your life - to see what is out of balance.   To do this honestly and thoroughly isn't easy.   But it's necessary.

In fact it's a must – much more of this is in Chapter 5. As a child I had gone to the doctors to see if he could make me better. But this time was different – I needed to make me better. It was my job. My responsibility. Down to me. Good. Who better to take charge of my health than me?

But how was I going to do this when I knew nothing about cancer? By falling back on what I DID know.

In my professional life I had been accustomed to assessing proposals and business cases. Analysing information and options, and selecting which would be the best course of action. These were the skills I had practised for years and years. I had lots of experience to draw on, it's what I knew how to do. So that's what I did.

There were other aspects of my professional life which influenced my thinking. I had worked in financial services for many years. In this world, there are tied agents, and also Independent Financial Advisers. (IFA's). The tied agent can only advise on the policies of the company they work for, even if it isn't actually the best thing for you. Because they have no knowledge and are not trained on anything else. In contrast, IFA's look at the whole of the market, and advise you on the policy or contract that is best suited to your needs. In both cases, they have to do a detailed fact find before they can recommend anything.

I saw doctors as tied agents. All they had to offer was what they were trained in; chemo, radiotherapy, surgery, and hormone treatments and their "fact-find" focussed around the disease. They knew plenty about my tumours, but absolutely nothing at all about me as a person. They didn't ask if I smoked 80 a day. Or who else in my family had cancer. Or anything else really. It surprised me that they could move to a treatment plan with such significant and serious side effects without knowing anything about me. In financial services we would have got the sack for doing that! I think that is why I didn't believe their prognosis. Although that was their experience, it had nothing at all to do with me. I really did wish I had a cancer IFA who could do a thorough job based on my specific needs.

But to be fair to doctors don't have anything else to offer. They are a product of the medical world's educational system and they haven't been trained to know about anything else. That is why they told me that there were no other options. It's probably more true to say that they didn't have any other options to offer, but that there are other options I could choose.

In my professional experience there are always options. For example in a business case, you always examine what would happen if you did nothing. Only then can you decide if taking any action at all is necessary or beneficial.

It isn't that I was in denial. I fully accepted that I had cancer. I accepted that I needed to do something about it. I just didn't know exactly what at this point. But I had experience of learning and absorbing new information – I had been involved in many projects where I initially had no detailed knowledge of the subject matter. But I was able to, and experienced in researching information, and then to challenge or corroborate what I was being told.

It helped me to see this whole cancer-thing as a project. It didn't feel quite as personal somehow and meant that I had a framework to follow that I knew and understood. Whilst others might have thought that I was bonkers, in actual fact I was being quite logical in my thinking. I knew it was a serious situation, and wanted to take the course of action that would "fit" me. The orthodox didn't (that's not to say for others it maybe the right route for them), so I had to do it my way (I think that's a cue for a song).

This summarises how I see the orthodox medicine viewpoint, and how my own views differed:

Orthodox	Maverick
• Focus on the tumours (symptoms)	• Focus on the whole person (cause)
• Treatment	• Recovery
• Poison the cancer to kill it accepting there will be collateral damage on healthy cells	• Boost the immune system to allow the body to heal itself
• Hate	• Love
• Battle, fight	• Journey, adventure
• The doctor is in charge	• You are in charge
• Probabilities	• Possibilities
• Prognosis	• Hope
• Sadness	• Humour
• Fear	• Acceptance
• No options	• Choices

Let me explain a little bit more. At a time when the overriding emotion is fear, I decided to embrace the opposite. I thought I should harness the thing which has caused wars, and crimes of passion, that has spawned many unforgettable poems and songs. The reason you would lay down your own life to save another. The most powerful emotion on the planet.

What is it? It's LOVE. I decided to LOVE myself better. To leave no room for hate, or regret, or unhappiness. To remember why I love life. To appreciate the support of the people I love. To do more of the things I love. The best prescription ever – love.

To love and thank the cancer for giving me the wake-up call, and the opportunity to fix it. (Not that I knew how at that point.)

Whilst I believed there must be choices and options, I didn't know what they were. As I researched cancer, I found lots of conflicting opinions from the medical world about the causes and treatment of cancer. Some thought it was a virus, others a fungus. And many other theories. If all these clever medical types couldn't agree, how on earth was I, the Cancer Virgin, supposed to know what to do?

I had no idea who was right or wrong. And I didn't have time to figure it out really. I thought how I would really like to consult the REAL experts, for me that meant the DIBs. Time was not on my side. I found out on 21st September 2012 that I had metastatic breast cancer. The letter came through telling me that I was booked in for my first chemotherapy appointment on 4th October 2012. I needed to make what could be a life or death decision within the next 13 days. The clock was ticking very loudly. What on earth should I do?

Should I do as I was advised by the medical experts, or go unilateral (go it alone)?

There feels to be immense pressure and urgency to follow what the doctors say. It feels as though you have no choice. But you do!

Just in case you need some proof, Macmillan publish a booklet called 'The Cancer Guide'. Here's an excerpt from it -

Consent

Before treatment begins you will be asked for your permission (consent) for the hospital staff to give you the treatment. No medical treatment can be given without your consent and before you are asked to sign the form, you should be given full information about

- *The type and extent of the treatment*
- *Its advantages and disadvantages*
- *Any significant risks or side effects*
- *Any other treatments that may be available*

On the next page...

If you don't want treatment

You are free to choose not to have the treatment that you have been offered. The staff can explain what may happen if you don't have it. It's essential to tell a doctor or the nurse in charge, so they can record your decision in your medical notes. You don't have to give a reason for not wanting treatment, but it can help to let the staff know your concerns so they can give you the best advice.

(I am telling you this not because I think you should turn treatment down necessarily, but to give you the confidence to take some time to consider your choices and options).

If this was the case, then what would I choose? I wanted to learn from DIBs but I didn't really know where to find them? Who had had a diagnosis exactly like mine, and was alive and kicking? I didn't know of anyone, and I didn't know where to look!

However, one thing I did have some knowledge about was the 3E centre near Stuttgart in Germany. I had been on a 'Mindstore for Business' course several years before all this, run by a man called Jack Black. This course had been quite profound for me – I learned about setting massive goals, and techniques to harness your ability to achieve them. And achieve them I did! At the time, I remember he was licensing someone at this 3E centre to use his techniques with people who have cancer. This all came flooding back to me, and I wondered how they had progressed in the years since. I was a huge fan of Mindstore, so if that was being used for the benefit of people with cancer, it had to be worth a look. I Googled it and found out that they were, indeed, still there.

The founders of the 3E Centre, Lothar Hirneise and Klaus Pertl, had studied cancer survivors around the world to see what the commonalities were – what did the people who survive cancer actually do? They had studied DIBs!!!!! They had years and years of research on what DIBs do. The 3E title comes from their findings, as there are 3 main themes which survivors follow. The first E is Energie – let's translate that as Mind and Spirit. The second E is Eliminieren – eliminating toxins. The third E is Essen – eating well. As a result of this research, they run a 5 week programme at their centre near Stuttgart in Germany to teach you what to do, to give you time to learn and absorb, and how to follow the Budwig protocol (more of this later). Their approach totally "fitted" me. I loved everything about it.

Here is what it says on the home page of their website -

'Welcome to a unique place.

At the 3E Centre you will learn about the right cancer treatment available to you and how to take pro-active steps to put your life into your own hands.

We offer our guests our extensive knowledge of the worlds' leading alternative cancer therapies. We explain which interventions and activities, based on your medical history, will be possible and appropriate for you. Together we begin your journey of healing, and the earlier you set off on this journey, the better!

As a privately owned company, we can offer you our expertise independently and unbiased. This independence makes it possible to show you everything that is on offer and gives you access to ALL information available.'

Hallelujah! I felt like I had come home! Having said that, I didn't know anyone with cancer who had been there, or what the results would be. To go there would take a huge leap of faith. Or, as some of my friends thought, to go there would be really stupid. What to do?

I had pressed that pause button, and been journalling like crazy to make sense of my thoughts and feelings about my diagnosis and treatment. One of the things I do to help me make decisions is to sleep on it. As you fall asleep, there is a change in your brain waves which takes you into Alpha State – in this state your logical left brain, and your creative right brain work in tandem. So as I fall asleep, I often ask my brain to figure things out for me. In this instance, I asked what I should do – the chemo tried and tested route, which was free on the NHS, and everyone was comfortable with and was telling me I must do. Or the 3E route, which although I didn't have any specific evidence that this was the right choice, and had no idea what the outcome would be, and I didn't have enough money for, every bone in my body felt it was the right decision. I went to sleep one night asking myself what to do. The morning after, when I woke, I knew. I just knew.

Against the advice and better wisdom of everyone around me, and taking that huge leap of faith, I turned down chemotherapy. I had several calls from the hospital who wanted to make sure that I knew exactly what I was doing. My family were really worried for my safety and whether I was making the right decision. At this stage I didn't know if it was the right decision or not. I had no idea what the outcome would be. But despite that, I did feel that it was the right course of action for me.

I had to find the faith, the courage, and the finances to make it happen. Which I did.

In October 2012 I packed my case and off I went to Deutschland. It was a phenomenal experience, and a huge investment of time, energy and money. It provided the foundation for me to learn how to heal myself. I don't believe that I would be where I am today without the help of the 3E Centre. I would recommend it to everyone with cancer as it teaches you so much, and provides the space and opportunity to work on yourself.

However, I do appreciate that it's not necessarily the course of action everyone would be willing, or able to take. But, even if that's a step too far, then you do still need to do something. Which is why I have written this book, to hopefully help you to make more informed decisions on what that is.

On my return home in November 2012, I made massive changes in my life, and followed what I had learned. I stopped working to concentrate on wellness. I worked on my state of mind every day. I followed the Budwig protocol from the work of Johanna Budwig, the eminent German biochemist (more of this later). I took many supplements, and tried many treatments and therapies. Everything I had learned at the 3E Centre I did religiously, and to the letter, for 7 months after diagnosis. (Since then, I have learned more and added to it, and adapted what I do to fit in with my lifestyle. I do most of the things I should, most of the time, but don't get too stressed about doing it 100% every single day, as it was providing a new pressure and stress in my life which I didn't need.)

In this book I will share with you what I do, what I've learned and why it's important. I am NOT saying that you should do exactly the same. Absolutely not. But it will give you some insight and pointers about what you can include in your own wellness plan. Budwig is not the only protocol; there are others. But it is my chosen one. It can be confusing when you look at all the various protocols, so I decided to hang my hat on the one I had been "trained" in. As it's all turned out rather well, it seems that was a good decision!

The 3E experience was the foundation for me on which everything else I have done, and achieved, has been built. I cannot convey in written words the knowledge and care that I encountered, and how it built my confidence and belief in myself that I would be able to do this thing. I am still in touch with the people there, especially one of the co-founders, Klaus Pertl. I asked him to share with us a few words about his views on cancer and cancer treatments. Some people will find his views challenging. Controversial even. Not everyone will agree with them. His views are however based on many years' research and experience. We must be prepared to challenge the status quo if we are to make progress:

Cancer: entitlement thinking versus self-responsibility

"There are two ways to literally handle any type of demanding situation in our life. One is to leave it to others to solve it for me and to hope they will do the best for me. The other is to make it my own responsibility and to lead the process of solving it.

In cancer there is a big gap in knowledge and understanding what cancer is, what treatments are effective and what oneself can do in this entire healing process. Usually you have the experts who know so much, and the patient who knows so little. This automatically creates a massive imbalance and strong dependencies.

And it opens the doors for being exploited. It makes the one person feel wise and the other person feel hopeless.

After more than 17 years of speaking to professors, doctors, oncologists and people with cancer and having travelled to more than 40 countries in which we did visit more than 100 alternative cancer clinics we can safely say that none of the so called experts in the medical and scientific community knows exactly what cancer is, how it is developed and what treatments work the best. They have until this day (after more than 70 years of cancer research) only theories. So it is still more an art than science. Science would mean that you have a 100% predictability rate. And in cancer this is not the case. Nobody has a 100% predictability rate.

What we (Lothar Hirneise and Klaus Pertl) have done is to find a way to get more clarity about how cancer CAN be cured. So what we did was to speak to as many cancer survivors as possible. And we still do that today. And here we do get some very clear facts that cannot be ignored. We found a number of important things that those people have done which have all been integrated in our 3E-Programme in Buoch/ Germany.

One of the points we found is that they take on 100% responsibility for their health. They become the leader. They stop being the victim of cancer. They start getting informed. They read up on cancer, they speak to experts from all areas of the healing professions to then assess all the data they have collected, and then make their decision; what for them, is the best way forward.

And Nina is clearly one of those exceptional people who knows that her own health has to be her own responsibility. Others clearly can give advice, offer solutions, give suggestions etc., but Nina then looked at all the data, looked at what she felt was right for her and then she decided what she wanted to do.

The old days when we went to a car dealer to buy a new car and trust that person completely are hopefully gone. Because we have learned and understood that those car dealers did very often have their own agenda in mind when talking to a potential buyer. The internet has helped to educate us better about how and where to buy a good car. The same thing we need to do when it comes to cancer. We cannot go to just one oncologist and trust that he or she knows it best.

So, what's possible if you take on the responsibility for your healing process?

Firstly, you become a much more equal partner in your cancer treatment. You and your therapist, oncologist etc. should be partners. It cannot be the responsibility of the oncologist to save your life. That is your responsibility because it is your life. You need to play the biggest role. If your oncologist makes the wrong decision for you, he or she is not suffering. You are.

Secondly, you start to ask more, and certainly also better questions, about cancer diagnostics and treatments. Knowledge is strength and can save your life. For example in Germany they discovered that 40% of chemotherapy for women with breast cancer was unnecessary. 22,000 women per annum could be spared that very aggressive and dangerous treatment. Ask more questions. And then some more questions. Then, only then when you have all the answers and information, you can make a truly informed decision what is acceptable to you, or what is not.

Thirdly, you face also the necessary tougher questions such as what are the real side effects and what are the best and worst outcomes. You need to know what the downside is. If someone would tell you that a very tough treatment with strong negative side effects will increase your chance of increasing your life expectancy by 30% then this does not mean a lot. 30% of what? If you would know the normal life expectancy is 6 months then you can make a much better assessment. Would you now for 2 additional months (that is what the 30% in this example means) take on all those negative side effects? Whatever is offered to you, you need to know those details. This is an important key element to make the right decision for you. Again to help you to better understand what you are willing to accept and what not.

Fourthly, conventionally trained oncologists do not know a lot about all the alternative cancer therapies that are effective outside of their local area. This is understandable, mainly because they are not paid to understand them, they are not attending training courses in those alternative treatments and it is certainly not part of the conventional medical training. They generally lack the time and often the motivation to spend their valuable free time to better understand and learn more about those alternatives. But here is an important truth: alternative therapies work! They have their validity because they work. There is sufficient proof. Naturally like the conventional therapies they do not work all of the time and not for everyone. But they do work. We have seen personally more than 100 alternative cancer clinics in more than 40 countries worldwide. Those are just the tip of the iceberg. And in all of those clinics we have met with real medical doctors. They are not fakes. They are real. It does make sense to learn more about them, because remember your oncologist will not know about them and will not spend time learning about them.

Fifth, up to this date it is still "ethically" prohibited to do comparative studies between conventional oncological therapies (such as operations, chemotherapy, radiation) and non-conventional therapies (such as our 3E Programme - Gerson, Galvano). So for medical professionals and cancer patients alike there are no official studies available. Not that the non-conventional community would not want to conduct studies, it is rather that a small group of very influential decision makers in the national health services still think it is unethical to do such comparative studies. So that means that the only way to hear about the success of other therapies is to speak directly (phone, email, or a personal visit) to those alternative therapy providers. I think a good idea is to visit them. And then ask them a lot of questions and get their data first hand. That is the only way you can find out the effectiveness of those therapies.

This all sounds like a lot of work. But please remember, you cannot just go to the car dealer and ask him what car he would recommend. That is clearly not a smart way forward.

Yes, cancer can be healed. There's clearly hope and with the mind-set of "this is my responsibility to decide what is the best therapy for me", you'll find the best therapies for you.

Nina is a great example and role model for this. In my thinking you cannot leave such an important thing to others.

Klaus Pertl
Co-founder 3E Centre
www.3e-centre.com

Another person who influenced my thinking massively in the early days of my diagnosis, is my friend Kimm Fearnley. I met Kimm on a Speaker Bootcamp, just before I found out I had cancer. She spoke about her work as a healer – and I was fascinated. Even though it was maybe a little woo-woo for me at that point in time. Her words were calm and helpful at a time when I was feeling afraid, so I asked her to share her views with us.

"We have all heard others or even ourselves say things like "I've got a headache after a rotten day at work" or "all that stress will give you a stroke"; "You need to relax or you will have a nervous breakdown" or "she died of a broken heart". Familiar? Of course! We hear and make statements like this all the time, but do we really understand what it is we are saying?

Do we really understand what the experts say when they dole out the chances of recovering from serious illness by saying: "Much will depend on your attitude or positivity"?

Responses to experiences and situations have a physical effect on our bodies. The bad day came BEFORE the headache, the emotional response caused the broken heart, and the response to a stressful problem causes the stroke. Likewise we know that a person who approaches a serious illness like cancer has a greater chance of survival if they choose a positive attitude, even the doctors say so!

How do placebos work? They make us believe we are receiving treatment and then we get well. It is a choice, a decision we take to believe something or to choose to respond differently. We are aware of negative emotional experiences such as fear and the effect these responses can have on the body because we FEEL a physical response in the form of stomach churning, being sick, or having to rush to the toilet, but actually NOTHING has happened other than the anticipation of something bad, but the body responds to our thoughts and emotions.

Likewise we are all aware of how happy and positive we can feel when good and exciting things happen; the body produces endorphins, we feel exhilarated, our skin glows etc. All of this proves that the way we choose to respond to everything that happens in our lives, big or small, has an impact on our physical bodies. Changing our emotional responses, learning to relax and let things go, will help stop illness growing in our bodies. Choosing to be well, choosing not to respond negatively to the bad day, not allowing jealously, greed, ego, anger or any other negative emotions to take hold of us, will help us toward good physical health -not just mental health. The two are entwined. If the mind is at peace, the body will respond too. Understanding and changing our emotional responses is crucial.

Asking ourselves WHY we feel or act a certain way, recognising these physical feelings and understanding we are each the master of our own lives and, unless we are a child, no one can make us do anything we don't want to do. It's true! You can right now, right this minute, walk away, dance naked in the street, or sing in the office. ANYTHING! No one can stop you, except you!

BE the master of your own life, change your responses now. Think well, live well."

Kimm Fearnley
Speaker, Healer

Interestingly, even though we three, Klaus, Kimm and I, come from different backgrounds, places and experiences, the message could not be clearer.

Take charge...

It's your life
It's your health
It's your future

CHAPTER 4 – YOUR TREATMENT PLAN – OPTIONS AND CHOICES

You have been doing the internal work – hitting the pause button, taking time to digest and accept your new reality.

You're working on your positivity and making sure that you are in the right frame of mind to face this big adventure.

You know that the person responsible for your health, for your recovery, for your wellness, is YOU.

So now it's time to move on from the internal work, and look externally.

Where do you start? How on earth do you know what to do about your 'Treatment Plan'? Especially if, like me when I was diagnosed, you know nothing about cancer. As you will hear me say, time after time in this book, you need to start with your mind-set. It's not helpful to you if you stay feeling fearful or overwhelmed.

Treat it as a voyage of discovery, a learning experience, or an exploration. We're used to shopping around and researching to see what the best deal is for many things in life. We do it when we buy a car, or a holiday, or electrical goodies. So of course we should do it when it comes to something as important as this.

Don't assume that you already know exactly what is going to happen. The conventional plan will probably have been outlined to you already i.e. surgery, chemotherapy, radiotherapy, hormone treatment. That's what happened for me, after only about 10 minutes at the breast clinic! But remember that is just one approach and you may or may not want to follow it to the letter.

Even if you do follow the conventional route, you may want to develop a plan to ease the symptoms, the side effects of the treatment, and set you on the road to recovery. For example, chemo is extremely toxic so supporting your liver and detoxing would be a great thing to do.

You have choices. If you don't look any further, you may miss something really important. So get your curiosity on. Be open to learning. Get creative so that you generate more options for yourself. Options = choice. Having choices gives you power and some element of control. Which feels great when you are in a situation where it can seem that you haven't. I do need to give a word of caution here though. There is a lot of conflicting information out there about cancer and cancer treatments – some parties have a vested interest, and there are different perspectives and views. I don't believe that means we shouldn't look though. It means that we need to be aware of that. To challenge what we are told. To qualify the information, and to seek to corroborate it.

Depending how you are feeling, mentally and physically, this may seem a big ask. You may need to draft in a relative or friend with an enquiring mind and attention to detail to help you to navigate the masses of information. There are other ways of making it easier on yourself, and speeding up the process, such as engaging the services of your chosen expert to help you navigate the choices available.

Back to the job in hand. As I mentioned, once you are diagnosed with cancer, you will receive a treatment plan from your medical team. It may include chemotherapy, surgery, radiotherapy, or hormone treatments. For me this was a starting point; as I wasn't convinced that was the right route for me, I asked about other options. I was told that there were none. In actual fact, I think it's truer to say that they didn't have any alternatives to offer me. That doesn't mean that there aren't alternatives elsewhere. I didn't know that then, but I do now, and I think it's one of the most important lessons I've learned.

This is really important, especially when orthodox medicine says "you're incurable" or "there is nothing more we can do". It may be true that they can't do anything, but there are still many options that you can pursue yourself. I find this fact comforting. And empowering. Whatever happens, I know I can have a plan of action.

You may be very happy with the treatment plan proposed by your doctors. It seems alien to me to be so accepting without researching and challenging first, but I do realise that not everyone is like me. It took me a while to realise that though. I was absolutely dead set against systemic chemotherapy when I was first diagnosed, and almost couldn't understand why others didn't feel the same. Later on, I remember reading the book "Now and Forever" by the singer Bernie Nolan, just after she had died from metastatic breast cancer. The book describes a time when she was unable to carry on with chemotherapy, because her blood counts were low. She said that she was really scared when she wasn't on chemo, as she could imagine the tumours growing unchecked, and felt that she was fighting it when she was having chemo. Whereas I saw it as poisoning my body, and wiping out my immune system at a time I needed it most. The reason I mention this is that we all feel differently. Just because one course of action is right for me, that doesn't mean it would be the right one for you. I would however encourage you to be well informed. Become one of the experts on your team, understand the treatment itself and exactly what it entails, its side effects and results. Also, find out any other options you could consider. Only then should you give your consent to the treatment plan.

Remember that you do have the right to say no to any or all of the plans or procedures; it's your choice, even though it doesn't always feel that way.

When it comes to orthodox medicine, there are many brilliant sources of information such as Macmillan, Cancer Research UK, and other (cancer specific) charities such as Breast Cancer Care. Many hospitals will assign a specialist nurse to support you who can be an invaluable source of information and support. Always remember though that their knowledge and training will not include the complementary and alternative options, and they are therefore likely to be dismissive of them.

Despite my initial misgivings about my treatment, I have always considered the doctors and oncologists as an important part of my team. As we all know, cancer is a moving feast, and just because you may not want a particular treatment at this point in time, circumstances and needs may change. I respect their knowledge and opinions. I just don't accept it as gospel. Some people are totally against orthodox medicine, and choose to use therapies which are usually described as "alternative". I have met many people in the last couple of years who have chosen to follow this path. For the first seven months after my diagnosis, I did exactly that. I turned down chemotherapy, and followed everything I had learned at the 3E Centre. For some people, that is enough and they find themselves in remission, or even cured. But because these interventions are non-toxic and relatively gentle, it takes time for them to work. Unfortunately my cancer was too far advanced, and time was something I was running out of. I therefore had to reconsider my plans. My options, as I saw them then, were to carry on with the natural approach, but I was deteriorating physically and I wasn't prepared to just sit by and let that happen. Another option would have been to say yes to the systemic chemotherapy offered to me through the NHS, but I still felt that it was too toxic, and would wreck my precious immune system. As neither of these options were acceptable to me, I needed to generate more choices.

This is when I really did need my cancer IFA, and luckily for me, I found her. Or rather the universe put her in my path. A total stranger who heard about me though a friend sent me a leaflet about 'Yes to Life'. They are a charity who support people with cancer who wish to take an integrative approach to their care. Just what I was looking for! I devoured the information from their website yestolife.org.uk. The site was jam-packed with information and resources and I scoured it all looking for inspiration. I also rang the helpline, and talked through my situation and what I was looking for. This is how I came across Patricia Peat, of Cancer Options (canceroptions.co.uk). She was it! My cancer IFA who could scan the whole of the market, and after understanding my needs, could help me find the right solution. Halle-flippin-lujah!

This was a huge turning point in my adventure. I had felt really alone and isolated, with the 3E Centre so far away, and not knowing anyone else following a similar path. But, now I wasn't alone. I had some people, experts and resources, who thought like I did. We humans are pack animals, and feel much happier and safer when we're not alone. This was certainly true for me. I feel very thankful for finding 'Yes to Life', and 'Cancer Options'. Without them, I don't believe I would be where I am today.

Having found my IFA, I quickly arranged a consultation. This was in March 2013, around the time of my birthday when I was fading fast. She listened to what I was experiencing, and what I was looking for. She explored various options for treatments, and it felt great to have some options and choices again, even in my dire circumstances. Her extensive knowledge, matter-of-factness and quiet confidence was catching. And I loved her dry-humour too. I felt that we really understood each other.

She agreed that I needed to do something else, quite quickly. I was not in great shape physically at all. I had fluid on my lungs and was having trouble breathing, and therefore couldn't walk very far. The tumour in my breast had grown considerably. It was ulcerating and about to break through the skin. The tumour in my lymph under my right arm was extremely painful, restricting my movement. My breast bone was extremely painful, and I was having trouble getting comfortable which was affecting my sleep. All in all I was feeling very delicate. I felt that I was fading a little more every single day.

One of the things Patricia mentioned to me was a means of administering chemotherapy in a more targeted way – called Trans Arterial Chemo Embolisation (T.A.C.E.), available in Germany. I remembered that the 3E team had mentioned this to me the previous October as a possible option should I need it, due to the advanced stage of my cancer. I was therefore very open to listening about it, and able to take an immediate decision to go for it.

Patricia also suggested other supplements and therapies that would help me and alleviate the worst of my symptoms. This range of treatments illustrated perfectly the broad spectrum of her knowledge and recommendations. On the one hand I was scooting off to Prof Vogl in Frankfurt for cutting edge treatment. And on the other I was preparing a turmeric paste to apply to comfort the ulcerating skin (I have the yellow-stained PJ's and sheets to prove it!).

Although I had started off my treatment down the "alternative" route, I knew I had to do something else, and readily agreed to adding in this T.A.C.E. treatment.

I did feel a bit of a failure though. I had read so many books of people who had been cured after juicing, or cannabis, or a miracle happening, so I did feel a bit of an underachiever. But I knew I had to be pragmatic about it. A girl's gotta do what a girl's gotta do. And I was more than ready to do it. In the case of alternative vs. orthodox medicine, I know exactly where I stand. It's with a foot in every camp! Using the best of orthodox and complementary (which I personally prefer to the term alternative) therapies as needed. The term used for this is integrative medicine.

Integrative – *"combining or coordinating separate elements so as to provide a harmonious interrelated whole"*. Ooh yes please, I will have me some of that.

Cancer is a complex disease. There isn't one single silver bullet to cure it – I chose to use a many pronged attack. I believe that it's this integrative approach that has got me where I am today. What makes me think that? On my many visits to Frankfurt (I had eight treatments in all during 2013) I saw people on the T.A.C.E. treatment who didn't improve month-on-month like me.

I know that the other work I'd done on my health and mind using what I learned at the 3E Centre is what made the difference. I appreciate that is not exactly scientific proof, but it is what I believe and know if my heart of hearts to be true.

My recommendation for your treatment plan is that you too take an integrative approach – with your choice of orthodox and complementary treatments included in it.

There are some brilliant resources for information on integrative medicine. Here are the ones which I personally have used, and highly recommend -

3E Centre - www.3e-centre.com

Yes to Life - www.yestolife.org.uk

Cancer Options - www.canceroptions.co.uk

Cancer Active - www.canceractive.com

Facebook groups; ninajoyspeaker, Cancer Mavericks, and Cancerucan.

As Patricia Peat (my IFA, or Guru as I like to call her) has played such a significant part in my story, I asked for her to share her views on dealing with cancer.

Cancer Options

Cancer Options is a service that was established in 2000 by Patricia Peat a former oncology nurse. The aim of the Cancer Options service is to provide the information, discussion, support, and perspective that will allow someone dealing with cancer to achieve the following:

An awareness of other viable approaches to supporting the body to enable it to work at its optimum against cancer cells

An appreciation of how important an individual is and how much they can achieve themselves in managing cancer and enabling the body to heal

A sense of purpose, positivity and empowerment so that you can take charge of the situation and influence all elements of recovery.

"We firmly believe in and trust the power our clients have to bring out the physical and psychological changes necessary to see dealing with cancer for what it is.

What it isn't is putting yourself in the position of having someone else in charge of you. We have created modern medicine as a system where we present ourselves to the doctors for them to 'get us better' and make the decisions that will get us there. They use the drugs that the drug companies say work best and some attempts are made at moderating the side effects.

Prognoses are given on the basis of what those drugs will achieve, you will live for as long as a doctor says he or she can keep you alive – seeing anything wrong with this picture?

There is little about modern medicine which is healing.

There is little asking the questions – how did I get here?

What contributed to my developing cancer?
Are there contributing factors, imbalances, viruses, that need putting right, to enable me to heal?

There is little that says – "here is the massive role you can play in your own recovery".

Epigenetics is a science which shows us that expression of genes is not fixed and is effected by everything that happens to us on a daily basis, physically and psychologically you can shape your future.

At Cancer Options we don't believe one approach is better than another, we put everything on the table, CAM (complementary and alternative medicine), nutrition, new drugs, clinical trials, treatments working around the world. If it works, and is not harmful it's up for consideration.

If you are having orthodox treatments we will provide you with the best support to get you through unscathed and ready to hit the ground running on the most important phase of the treatment; what you can do for yourself!

We have had the privilege of seeing many people, for many years, healing themselves, when everyone around them was being negative. We believe given the right information and tools people can become their own healers.

www.canceroptions.co.uk

Wow. Hopefully you can start to see how and why I seem to have achieved what conventional medicine thought impossible.

So far in the book, there have been contributions from three of the people who have played a significant part in my story – Klaus Pertl from the 3E Centre, Kimm Fearnley, a speaker and healer, from The Happiness Centre, and Patricia Peat; an ex-oncology nurse, now cancer consultant with Cancer Options. Each of them has a very different background and perspective, and yet their overall message is strikingly similar.

There is a saying that if you hear something once you should listen to it. That if you hear something twice, you should really listen. And if you hear something three times, it's time to act on it.

We have established that you are the one responsible for your own health, recovery and wellness.

Who better to be in charge?

You will still need others to work with you though, it's the pack animal thing. As the Macmillan ad states so poignantly, no-one should face cancer alone. Certainly, when it comes to your treatment plan, you will need the support and expertise of many people.

You may be the Captain, but you need to assemble your crew to work alongside and support you:

- Hospital team – consultant, oncologist, specialist nurse, surgeon etc.

Whether you go alternative, orthodox, or integrated, you will need assessing and looking after medically at some point. That may not be now, and the need may be lesser or greater over time, but you need the security of having a good medical team in your corner. I have always prepared for my appointments in the same way as I would for an important meeting. I make notes – what are my objectives for the meeting, what questions would I like to ask? I actually make myself a little agenda to follow. One of the most difficult situations is when deciding to turn down the treatment on offer, and opting for an alternative course of action, such as when I turned down chemo here, and went to Frankfurt for T.A.C.E.

My approach with my oncologist was quite factual e.g. *I have researched x and y, and decided that I need to do x which is not available here at this hospital. The support I need from you is a, b and c, and I am presuming that you will be happy to continue to oversee my care. Thank you. (finish with a beaming smile!)* It's what we call in sales jargon "a presumptive close". It has worked well for me so far!

REMEMBER: You need to keep your doc on side. Make sure you prepare especially well for the meeting. Be confident. It's reasonable to assume that you will have their support, but don't seek approval – they are unlikely to be familiar with the treatments, so it's not fair to expect them to endorse what you are doing. I very rarely even tell my doctors what I am doing, so it cannot "upset" them, and I am not disappointed by their reaction.

- Your Cancer IFA/integrated specialist

This has been one of the most important choices I've made. I highly recommend Patricia Peat of Cancer Options, to anyone choosing an integrated treatment plan.

There are others, such as Dana Flavin, Rosie Daniels, Xandria Williams. 'Yes to Life' is a great resource to find options.

It's important that you seek out the one which is right for you. Do you like their approach, the way they communicate with you, do you have a high level of trust in their expertise? Have a good old look at what they do, perhaps speak to others who have DIBbed.

- Cheerleaders – your family, friends, and supporters, including virtual ones on Facebook & Twitter.

Your cancer diagnosis will change your relationships. You are likely to lose some friends. That is OK. If they can't hack it, they need to move on. They probably wouldn't be much support to you anyway, and you have enough to do for yourself without expending your energy on others. But other people, sometimes the ones you would have least expected to, will step up and be there for you. Seek out the people who make you feel good, and confident about the choices you are making. You need to surround yourself with love, and positivity to get you through this.

You can bolster your gang with the most wonderful people by going virtual. The information and support I have had through Facebook (especially Fiona Shakeeela Burns group Cancerucan), and Twitter has been immense. Plus it's accessible exactly when you need it; any time of day or night.

• Therapists – to cope with the side effects of treatment, or as part of your treatment plan (more in Chapter 8)

Choosing the right people (right for you that is) will make a huge difference to your cancer adventure. Again, do your research, see who you are drawn to, and trust your instincts. If there is a particular therapy, or person that you are drawn to, go with that. Trust yourself to choose the right thing for yourself.

- Your GP

  I haven't seen my GP very often, because as strange as it sounds, I haven't really been ill as such. But even so it's good to keep your local doc in the loop, so that if you do need anything at any time, he or she is familiar with your circumstances.

I decided not to go into detail here about exactly what supplements I am taking. I don't want to imply that what I am taking is what everyone else should do. Your cancer will be different to mine. Also, I change my supplements from time to time, so the information would soon be out of date. Patricia and I are great believers in mixing it up. Cancer adapts, so we need to be one or more steps ahead, to keep it guessing. There are some principles though that you need to follow, which are universal.

You need supplements which will do the following
- Fight cancer (e.g., I3C, reservatrol, reishi mushrooms)
- Boost your immune system (e.g., Vit C and E and zinc)
- Look after your liver (e.g., milk thistle, magnesium, Vit K)
- Supplement your overall health and energy (e.g., Vit D, ginseng)

You may have some other needs specific to your cancer, for example, as I have cancer in my bones I take something to strengthen them. I also have had some adrenal fatigue so I have been taking supplements to help my energy levels. This is all totally tailored and personal to me, and yours should be too.

I would encourage you to see a professional to draw up your own personal plan, as I did with Cancer Options.

If for any reason you don't want to consult a professional (I can't imagine why that would be) and you want to DIY, the best source of information I have found is Chris Woolams site www.canceractive.com and his book "Everything You Need to Know to Help you Beat Cancer – The Ultimate Guide for People Who Have Cancer and Everyone Who Wants to Prevent It."

Chapter 5 – MIND-SET - IT ALL STARTS HERE

As you know, the team at the 3E Centre have studied cancer survivors around the world to find out what the commonalities are – what do people who survive cancer actually do? The first E of the 3, is Energie, which translates literally as energy, but a better interpretation would be Mind and Spirit - positive thoughts and focus, living a life with purpose, love and happiness.

I totally buy into the fact that this is crucial, let me tell you why.

Firstly, I guess my natural disposition is a positive one. My upbringing reinforced that – both my parents were very positive people to be around. One of the first books my dad ever shared with me was 'Jonathan Livingston Seagull'. I loved that book. It tells of a seagull who refuses to conform. He should have been 'Jonathan Maverick Seagull!' He pushes himself to learn, and eventually becomes a teacher of other seagulls. You have to read it to understand I guess. But suffice to say that it had a profound effect on me.

Then early in my career with the Halifax, I worked in the Training Department, and was introduced to many self-development gurus, such as Stephen Covey, Dale Carnegie, and latterly Jack Black of Mindstore, and Mike Dooley. I was always learning, absorbing that we have the power mentally to achieve whatever we wish to achieve.

Speaking of gurus - one of my favourite people on the planet is Deepak Chopra. I have read many of his books over the years, and they have blown my mind! One of the first ones I read was 'Ageless Body, Timeless Mind'. This explains about the mind/body connection, and how what we think affects the body. So I was already totally sold on that being true. Since my diagnosis, I have read some other books which have totally cemented that view. I highly recommend that you read more if there is any doubt in your mind at all, that your thoughts can, and do, affect your health and wellness.

My two favourites are 'How Your Mind Can Heal Your Body' by Dr David Hamilton, and 'Mind over Medicine' by Dr Lissa Rankin. As you can see, they are both written by Doctors, and provide scientific proof about the mind/body connection.

As well as the reading, I did lots of research into the power of happiness and positivity when I first became a professional speaker. Yet another reason why I totally accepted that my state of mind was crucial. I also learned quite a bit about the brain. That your thoughts develop neural pathways – so if you work at thinking positively and being happy, that becomes your pattern of thinking. I also learned about neuroplasticity –

that new pathways can be formed. So if you are a pessimistic, glass half empty kind of a person, you can, by working at it, develop new neural pathways. How cool is that? We are not stuck with what we've got. The mind is incredible – do you know it can't tell the difference between imagination and reality? This is great. So by imagining, or visualising, our brains can think it is really happening.

I genuinely feel as though the Universe was getting me ready for the challenges to come. I had spent a lifetime learning and absorbing and understanding just how much we can achieve, and every single thing we achieve, however big, it all began with just a thought!

I talked in Chapter 2 about getting into a positive frame of mind when you are first diagnosed. That's a good start, but there is more real work to be done on your frame of mind once you have got through that initial period, and this is what I will cover in this chapter.

It is not a chapter to read through quickly. Each exercise needs working through, multiple times. Until you feel you have real clarity and understanding on the way forward.

This is the most crucial part of your recovery. You might think what on earth has all this got to do with healing? It has everything to do with healing – we are not just healing from the disease, but aiming to recover and come back better than ever. You can only do that if you have solid foundations. This chapter builds those foundations.

Don't rush, don't skimp. Enjoy the process of discovery, and get excited about where this might take you.

Life after a cancer diagnosis can feel a lonely, scary, and sad place. Which is exactly what you don't need on many levels. You therefore need to counteract this so that you stay in the positive frame of mind you need to be in.   How? This is how:-

Vitamin P

You may not be aware of Vitamin P. You can't buy it in a health food store, yet it's one you need to take every single day of your life, it's as important as the air we breathe. The P stands for Positivity, or Pleasure, or Play. Or if you're really lucky, Passion.

We know the things that have been proven to make us more Positive (if you've forgotten, take a peek at the '10 Keys to Happier Living' at www.actionforhappiness.org). Many of them are really simple to slot into everyday life, for example, taking a walk outside, doing something for others, connecting with people.

What are the things that give you Pleasure? Mine include a soak in a hot bath, being by the sea (preferably somewhere warm), getting dressed up to the nines and going out with the people I love, and listening to music in the car so loud it makes my ears bleed.

What are your favourite things, what gives you Pleasure and makes your heart sing – have you forgotten in the busyness of life? You need to remember! And are you making time to do them? Take some time to re-connect with what they are. Get that journal out!

What do you like to Play at? Is it a game in the park with your children, or doggies? Is it sneaking a go on the swings? Going for a splash in the swimming pool, a go on the trampoline, a plonkety plonk, on a piano, making a pot or plate, or are you happiest with crayons and a colouring book? Go on - indulge your inner child, a bit of playfulness and being silly does us good.

What fires your Passion? A hobby or cause that is close to your heart? Or is it a date night or romantic weekend with your boy or girlfriend/lover/husband or wife? The really good news is that sex is great for your health too, so make time to get intimate. If you don't have a partner, make sure that you get the physical contact we humans crave – give lots of hugs, treat yourself to a sensual massage.

Are you spending time on these things? Possibly not. We all get caught up in the routine of life don't we? Doing all the things we should do/have to/ought to. Well at the top of your 'To Do List' now is taking your Vitamin P. You owe it to yourself and your future health and happiness.

Looking after our frame of mind is important. The Vitamin P gets you in the right place to do the real mental work that needs facing up to in the wake of your cancer diagnosis. And make no mistake, it is work. If you do it honestly and deeply enough. Are you ready?

Here goes:-

I see cancer as a massive wake up call. It's your body's way of saying "Oi! This is not working for me, something needs to change!"

What we need to do now is to hit the pause button again, to work out what that something is.

Maybe you know already, maybe you don't. Let's work through some questions which will help you identify what's really going on for you.

You need to dig deep and spend some time considering each of these questions. Perhaps meditate while you consider each one in turn, over time, to do it justice. That Journal needs to come out again – this is really important stuff.

This is **vitally** important if you are to change your future.

Q Who is the person I have become?
Do an assessment of yourself, being as objective as you can, but totally without blame or criticism.
Think about your emotions and what motivates you.

Q What needs to stop?

What is going on in your life - at home, at work, at play, that isn't working for you?

What needs to stop, or change dramatically?

What makes you feel anxious – is it every Sunday evening when you contemplate work the next day? Is it money? Is it a relationship which is no longer serving you?

What habits and thought patterns would you like to stop?

What causes you stress or anxiety? Ask yourself "What do I need to let go of?"

Q What caused the cancer in my life? (This is a biggie!)

What's your body objecting to?

What is it trying to tell you?

What do you need to face up to?

Is there some past trauma or baggage you need to deal with?

What causes you stress, what agitates you?

Q Who am I really, at the very core of my being?

What is your authentic self?

What is the purpose in your life?

What creates happiness and purpose in your life?

What is the world waiting for from you?

Ask yourself "What do I think, say and do when I am being the real me? What gives me quality of life, strength, and motivation?"

Q What should come into my life?

How will you create health? What are the new activities and behaviours of the real you? What new ways of living and new habits do you want?

Those questions may look deceptively simple, but they are the key to future change. If the life you have been living has resulted in cancer, you do need change. You need to accept and embrace that fact, and figure out what those changes should be.

You can work on these each day, try taking 15 minutes to work on each question, and write down all your thoughts in your journal, and all the ideas that come to mind. You can come back to them again and again, to make sure you are moving in the right direction.

If you find it too difficult to do this work on your own, it may be helpful to work with a therapist (more in Chapter 8).

There are some other techniques I use which may help you:-

Journalling

As you have already seen, I am a big fan of the journal, hence why I decided to produce one to make all these processes easier for you (you can buy it from oodlebooks. com) – but of course any notepad will do, just make sure you actively engage in following the questions I have suggested and writing down all your answers. There are very few situations in life that are not made better by writing about them. Many of the exercises I used myself, and now recommend, involve writing.

In the early days after my diagnosis, I did a daily journal to help me comprehend this enormous news, and make sense of it. I then moved to an online version of it, my blog at ninajoy.com. I have also told my story in my first book 'The Adventures of a Cancer Maverick' as mentioned earlier. Writing down my thoughts, hopes, dreams and fears has helped me enormously. It also provides a brilliant record so that I can recognise what progress I've made, and how far I've come.

Plus it's a vehicle to share with others if you choose to – to help those close to you understand what's going on, or others in similar circumstances to learn from your experiences.

There are some other exercises I have done which may help you to understand yourself and your life better:-

A Day of Silence
For a full 24 hours remain in complete silence. Do not speak to anyone in person, or on the phone, by text or chat. In silence, it is easier to hear and feel intuition.

Your tasks for the day

Get clarity and focus – what do you want?

Think about being happy with yourself and your life

Let go, and forgive

Be grateful

Use a journal, make notes of your thoughts and feelings

Look out for synchronicity and signs –be open to what you see, hear and feel. Is there a message for you?

Read things that inspire you

Get outdoors into nature and go for a long walk. Spend time looking around, seeing if you notice anything

If you have any unfinished business, write a letter to that individual to bring closure. Then burn it, and watch it go up in smoke.

Have fun, and enjoy this special day which is just for you.

Meditating or Mindfulness

This is the ultimate pause button. It creates the time and space to get in touch with your thoughts and feelings, and really listen and tap into your innermost feelings. I recommend that everyone does this every single day. Even if you only do 10 or 15 minutes. Try it. See what you think. If you don't know how to meditate (I didn't) you can learn by attending classes, or there are CDs, or Apps, which will guide you. One of my favourite Apps is Buddhify.

You can get started with this really simple technique –

Choose something you already do every day, like brushing your teeth, or having your morning cup of coffee. The next time you do it, really focus on it. Bring your awareness to what you are doing using all your senses.

If you're having coffee, make it in your favourite china beaker, savour the aroma, feel the heat of the cup in your hands, enjoy the flavour, and feel the warmth of the liquid as you swallow. When you bring all your senses to a task and focus on this, you're in the present moment. That's the essence of meditation or mindfulness. Try it!

Dreams

I find dreaming a really helpful way of tapping into my innermost thoughts. You might find that you can't remember your dreams, but with practice you will get better at it. If there is something on my mind, as I fall asleep, I ask my subconscious to work on the question for me. For example, "what needs to stop in my life? Have a notebook (yes, that journal again!) at the side of your bed, and as soon as you wake up, jot down anything you remember about your dream. There may not be a literal answer, but there may be a symbolic message or a sign. If you can't see it yourself, try talking about the dream with someone who knows you well, who you trust, as they may have an interesting perspective on what they think it is trying to tell you.

Visualising

One of the many things I learned at the 3E Centre was how to visualise. It was apparent in those sessions that not everyone finds it easy to visualise. It comes quite easy to me - it's a bit like daydreaming-on-purpose, and I have never had a problem with daydreaming I can tell you!

I am going to share one of my healing visualisations so that you understand how they can work. This might be something you could then adapt to your own circumstances, or share with someone who needs to get well. Or, if you want to use it to send healing my way, then that's fine too - all good wishes gratefully received. Always.

You already know my feelings about cancer – it's not

an "enemy", me and my body made it. So I don't feel a cancer "victim", I am not having a "battle" with cancer. The problem with battles is there is usually a winner and a loser, and that's not how I see it at all. I quite like the idea of a playful, fairy-tale like approach.

Which is why one of my early visualisations went like this:-

Do you know those snow globes which have a winter scene, and then when you shake them, the snow blizzards. Well I imagine, that my blood looks very like that blizzard, but the big snowflakes are the white cells in my blood, there to fight illness and infection.

These cells are pretty clever, they know where to go. Bodies are like that - if you cut your finger, they don't send the blood clotting and healing brigade to your toe, they know where they need to patrol.

First of all, they visit my lungs. They see that there is a small tumour in otherwise pink and healthy lungs. They ask the tumour what's going on. The tumour replies "it was all fine when I got here, I was ready to make myself at home. But since then the climate is much more unwelcoming - lots of detoxing and healthy food, plus some inhaler thing. I am feeling really out of place now".

The white cells sympathise with the changing situation, and ask if they can help by using their powers to help dislodge the tumour so it can dissolve and leave. "Yes please" says the tumour, and the white cells settle all over it, like snow, and as it dissolves the tumour disappears with it.

Next, they move on to my liver. They see the small tumour settled into what looks like a very pink, very healthy liver. They say hello, and ask what's going on. The tumour says "when I first arrived here it was lovely, lots of dark sadness, the liver was fed up of having to work hard with all those toxins and had no resistance to me moving in at all. Since then though, everything has changed! No toxins to speak of, lots of heat; especially in bed at night, which I HATE, and then to top it all off, a massive liver cleanse. It really is too much. The liver can regenerate you know, and at this rate, I'm not sure how long I can hold on!" The white cells sympathise with the tumour, and ask if it would like help to dissolve and move on. "Yes please! I'm exhausted!" says the tumour, and the white cells settle all over it like snow, and as it dissolves the tumour disappears with it.

The next stop then has to be the right breast. This is a very different scenario - a large well-established tumour which must have been there a while. The white cells introduce themselves to the tumour. The tumour says "you guys took your time to come and say hello". The cells say "yes, you're right. With the situation in this body, we weren't feeling too active, so we didn't get over here as quick as we would have liked. However, we are now feeling much brighter - you must have noticed some changes too?" The tumour replies "you're not kidding. We were getting really comfortable here, so much so had spread out into the lymph nodes, and even into the sternum. But now, it's not nearly so easy, and to tell the truth we are finding it a bit hard going".

The cells ask "so would you consider moving on?" "No chance, we've been here ages, and it was fine, it's only this last 5 weeks or so that it's been tricky, so I think we would like to wait and see what happens next. We've liked it here and would like to hang on. I suppose we could conserve a bit of energy by pulling back from the lymph, and the sternum. If this nutrition and detox thing carries on, we might than have to pull back further".

The white cells offer to help, and they settle like snow on all the cancer cells in the sternum, and in the lymph nodes to help them dissolve. They agree to review the situation in a month or so - if things carry on as they are, the white cells will be even stronger and more active, and the cancer cells less able to thrive. The cells wave bye, bye, to the breast tumour, and say "see you later". They know that there is unfinished business, and the white cells will be back.

Sounds funny. Bonkers even. It makes me giggle. At one time I would have dismissed it as hippy nonsense. But let me remind you that the tumours in my liver and lungs have not grown in the two years since I started doing this stuff. Obviously that doesn't mean that's purely down to visualising – I have been doing many other things too. But I do believe that it has contributed. It makes me feel that I am doing something to help myself. It makes me feel peaceful and calm, and that all will be well – so yes, it's doing something very positive.

Visualising can also be used to work on the big questions about your future.

Imagine a large white-framed mirror, and that you are looking at yourself in the future. Doing all the things you weren't doing before, being the YOU, you always wanted to be. Looking healthy and happy, fulfilling your purpose in life. See yourself, imagine what you'll be doing and hearing and feeling. Live it!

Gratitude

I mentioned this in Chapter 2, as it's the first thing I did to help me come to terms with my diagnosis, and get back to a more positive place. It also belongs in this chapter, as it's a tool to use on an ongoing basis. I defy anyone not to feel better when you dwell on what you're grateful for.

You can finish each day with three things you're grateful

for – in a journal, or on social media if you want to share. Or you can periodically do a list of as many things as you can think of, which sometimes throws up some surprises and new found appreciation for aspects of your life. Or, as a family, you can have a gratitude jar. Pop in a note of things you are grateful for, and make an occasion of opening it and sharing them on a significant date, perhaps a birthday, an anniversary or New Year's Eve.

Self-Confidence
It is vitally important that you believe in yourself, have the confidence that you can succeed in making changes in your life, and becoming healthy. A cancer diagnosis can make you feel more vulnerable, and knock the self-confidence you had. So it's worthwhile doing a bit of work on it. Time to get that journal out again!

- What have you succeeded at in the past? What are you proud of having done?
- What are your talents and unique abilities? What do your friends, family and colleagues admire about you? If you don't know, ask them! How do those talents help you to do what you want to do?
- Use the power of positive imagination/ visualisation
- Focus on progress; rather than perfection. Even if you haven't achieved everything you wanted to, recognise how far you have come.
- Use powerful affirmations in the present tense e.g. 'I am healthy, or I am returning to health and

getting better every day'. 'I am successful and have everything I need'.

- Make a long list of reasons why you know you can succeed
- How do you look at problems, failures? Put a positive interpretation on events e.g. it's just a temporary setback, I know I can do this just not in those circumstances, etc.
- Focus on the solution and your personal power to create the life you want
- Use the routines, discipline, and knowledge you already have, to tackle this issue in your life.

Forgiveness

Perhaps you have some regrets. A negative thought or experience. Maybe you did a bad thing, perhaps you've hurt somebody and would like to apologise and seek their forgiveness.

It's not always possible to do this – it maybe someone who is no longer alive, or you're no longer in touch with. Make a commitment to yourself to do what you have to do to feel better. Forgiveness is for you, not for anyone else necessarily. Forgiveness does not always mean reconciliation with the person who hurt you, or you hurt. What you are after is to find peace and closure.

The practice of forgiveness has been shown to reduce anger, hurt, depression, stress, and leads to greater feelings of peace, compassion, hope and self-confidence.

Practicing forgiveness leads to healthy relationships as well as physical health. It also influences our attitude which opens the heart to kindness and love.

This next technique is a great way to deal with seeking forgiveness.

It's a spiritual process from Dr Ihaleakala Hew Len, called Ho'oponopono. It works on the premise that we are all connected. If I have a thought, it goes out into the world, and someone may act on it on my behalf. It's deceptively simple, just four phrases, which you need to repeat until you feel a release from the negative thought or experience.

I am sorry

Please forgive me

Thank you

I love you

I did this exercise on my 'Day of Silence', and found it really powerful and emotional. I finally let go of something that had been bothering me for many years. Try it.

If there is someone you need to forgive, write them a letter. It can be as long as you like. You can even have a rant about what happened if it helps. You don't need to filter what you say as this is not a letter to be posted. It will help you express how you feel, to reach the peace and closure we mention above. By the end of the letter you need to say that you forgive them. And mean it. Re-read the letter when you've finished it. Recognise that the situation is over and cannot be changed. Consign it all to the past where it belongs. Feel the forgiveness. And then symbolically burn the letter. Poof! Gone. Over and done with. How good does that feel?

Walking outside in daylight

This is great for us on many levels – the Vitamin D, the fresh air, oxygen, and the appreciation of nature. But most of all it benefits the mind. It provides time and opportunity to be at one with yourself (do not plug yourself into any devices, this is time to observe, to enjoy to think). It's a great daily habit to get into.

To get even greater benefit, get tactile. Get up close and personal with a tree. I know – it sounds bonkers. But try it. Feel the bark,imagine how long it's been there, the people who have seen it, picnicked under it. If the temperature, and your self-consciousness allow, get barefoot on the grass. Feel the coolness underfoot, and the sensation of the blades of grass between your toes. These type of practices are known as 'earthing' – being connected to the energy of the earth. If you would like to know more about it, see www.earthing.

com . Sounding a bit woo-woo? Yes I know. But what I also know is, they feel good and as a bit of a hedonist I'm all for that!

Music

Is there a song or piece of music which makes you want to get up and dance? Or one that takes you back to a particular place and time? One that makes you happy, or another that reminds you of a sad time. Is there a piece which makes you feel serene and calm? Music has the power to stir the emotions within a few notes. Think of the national anthem when awarding medals at the Olympics. Or children singing Christmas carols.

Take time to listen to the music you love. Get a teenager to help you compile a playlist. I have a few for different occasions– relaxing, energising, and happy songs.

Physical activity

There is something about getting your bod moving that lifts the spirits and gets those endorphins pinging. What sort of physical activity do you enjoy? Maybe you like to cycle, or swim, or whack a ball. If you love the gym then do that. If you hate it, find something else. Find yourself a fitness buddy, or hit the park with your children and a Frisbee or a football. Do you love to dance? Try a salsa or belly-dancing class. It doesn't matter what it is you do, so long as you get moving, and enjoy it.

Choose who you mix with

The people you spend time with matter. You need them to believe in what you are doing, and to be there to support you. Be prepared to distance yourself from anyone who brings you down, makes you doubt your ability to heal, or is generally toxic. Your time is very precious, choose wisely who you spend it with.

This chapter is one you need to refer to time and time again. It is work that needs doing on an ongoing basis, so that you stay in a positive place, and are able to deal with anything else that arises.

YOU are the key to your recovery, so it's worth spending the time on YOU.

CHAPTER 6   THE NASTIES – LESS IN, MORE OUT

Pre-cancer I had no awareness of toxins at all. It just wasn't in my sphere of consciousness. I lived a thoroughly 21st century lifestyle and gave it no thought whatsoever. I wouldn't have known what was toxic to my body (beyond the blatantly obvious). I didn't even think about it.

I now know different. I know how important this is. The body is rather clever at coping with the toxins we expose it to, and pretty efficient at getting rid of toxins from the body, but it does have a breaking point. It's all about toxic load. So if you are bombarding your body with chemicals, your body may get to the point, when it's struggling, to detoxify. Whilst it would be impossible to live a toxin-free life, we can take steps to reduce what we take in, and help our bodies to be more efficient at detoxifying. With a greater awareness and knowledge, many of the measures are relatively simple to include in your lifestyle, without any major hassle.

So, why wouldn't you?

Here are the measures I take. It can be rather daunting to take on everything at once, figuring out what to do, sourcing supplies, buying what you need. I suggest you adopt one per week, picking off the ones you think are most important to you first. Unless you have cancer, in which case I recommend you do as much as you possibly can to protect and detox, on a daily basis. Your body is in crisis – it has enough on its plate, especially if you are undergoing treatment, so give it all the help you can, as soon as you can manage it.

NINA's ANTI- NASTIES TOP TIPS

This isn't an exhaustive list, but covers the major lifestyle areas of toxicity to avoid:-

- Avoid the obvious, the things we know are toxic – tobacco, alcohol, (prescription) drugs. I have had periods of abstaining from alcohol, but as I enjoy a cheeky glass of wine, I now have one if I want to. Well I am a Maverick after all! And remember it's about toxic load, so if I have alcohol, I will drink more water, and take even better care of my liver to make up for it. Johanna Budwig was okay about including a glass of champagne, or red wine, in your daily routine, so if Johanna says it's ok, that's good enough for me. I don't smoke, avoid others who do, and the only drug I am taking at the moment is Low Dose Naltrexone.

- Water – I drink only filtered water. I have a filter jug in the fridge, I stand it on a magnetic pad so that the water is ionised. www.magnetictherapy.co.uk Individual filters can be fitted onto each tap if you wish. When out and about, most bottled waters are in plastic, which is a no-no, so I carry water in a metal water bottle, or I have a water bottle with individual filters, so that I can fill and filter wherever

I am.

- Cosmetics –It has been estimated that women expose themselves to 515 chemicals a day source – *The Daily Mail* (mainly through the use of cosmetics and cleaning materials) It therefore makes sense to use natural and organic alternatives wherever possible. My favourite brands are Arbonne: www. arbonneinternational.co.uk and Tropic Skincare: www.tropicskincare.co.uk. Perfume is the biggest culprit in terms of number of chemicals. Personally though, I don't want to live in a world without Chanel perfume. So I compromise. On days when I am having some down-time, I go without perfume. Sometimes I spray it on my clothes, or tuck some perfume-soaked cotton wool into my bra. And then for special occasions I spray it on and really enjoy it. I have given up bubble baths, and soak in bicarbonate of soda or magnesium. Acrylic nails are a thing of the past. Learn to love your natural self.

- Cleaning materials are full of chemicals, so there's only one thing for it – give up cleaning! Or get a cleaner. They are the best solutions I think! If that's not an option, use natural cleaning agents such as bicarbonate of soda, and vinegar; or eco-friendly products such as Ecover or Method, and protect your skin by using rubber gloves.

- Food – buy organic whenever possible, including fruit and vegetables, meat fish and poultry and eggs. If your fruit and veg are not organic, wash thoroughly using an Ozone Generator (you can find one on Amazon).

- Avoid processed food and any packaged in plastic - this includes bottled water, and tin can linings.
- Avoid artificial air fresheners, dryer sheets, or fabric softeners - as you will be breathing them in. Try opening the windows instead, and hanging your washing outside – nothing smells better than that does it?
- Don't use non-stick pans, as it can contaminate food as you're cooking. Stainless steel or ceramic are better.
- Electromagnetic pollution –Electromagnetic (EMF) pollution is generated by most electrical appliances, electrical cables, hair dryers, electrical shavers, microwaves and mobile telephones. Some people believe it to be a common factor in most serious and long-term illnesses and psychological conditions.
- You need to keep the bedroom, in particular, clear of electrical appliances such as radio alarms, TV, and also mobile phones and tablets etc. If you must have wi-fi in the house (not recommended), then switch it off during the night when the body is resting and healing. The easiest way to do this is to put it on a timer. Also, you can obtain protective resonators from www.quantumk.co.uk - I have them on my watch, iPhone, iPad and laptop.
- Geopathic stress is another thing which was a new one on me. Apparently it's when the Earth's electromagnetic field becomes distorted. The Earth

resonates with an electromagnetic frequency. This natural resonance is distorted by sewers, water pipes, electricity, tunnels and underground railways and geological faults which creates geopathic stress. You can identify lines of disturbed earth energy currents by bringing in a professional dowser, or a healer who specialises in this field. I consulted with Caitlin Walsh and identified some areas of my house to avoid. I actually changed where I sleep, and where I usually sit as a result! www.caitlinhealer. com

- Grief, stress and troubles are all toxic to your system. (See the techniques in Chapters 2 and 6 for how to deal with these).

So, that's how to take less toxins into your body. Now let's look at how to get more toxins out.

DETOXING

We tend to think about a detox being an occasional thing that you do after a Christmas blow-out, or before your summer holidays. In actual fact, we need to make our bodies into detoxing power houses every day. They are already pretty good at doing this and many organs in the body are involved in detoxing – for example, liver, skin, colon, lungs, lymphatic system, and kidneys. However, they need help because of the world we live in. Think about it, thousands of chemicals are added to food and can be found in drinking water. Plants are sprayed with toxic chemicals, animals are injected with hormones and antibiotics and much of our food is genetically engineered, processed, refined, frozen and cooked. The potential for overload is huge, so we need to take action.

Here are the things I do to work with each of these organs to detox my body. Even during the 9 months I was on chemotherapy (which is extremely toxic) I sailed through it with minimum side effects, and recovered really quickly. I believe that these measures helped me to do that.

Liver

This is the Head Honcho of detoxification, breaking down or transforming substances like metabolic waste, drugs, alcohol and chemicals, so that they can be excreted. So the more you look after your liver, the better.

I use daily coffee enemas – it's believed that caffeine stimulates the liver to produce Glutathione S transferase, a chemical which is known to be the master detoxifier in our bodies. This Glutathione S transferase binds to toxins and the toxins are then released out of the body along with the coffee. Good huh! There is something about the term "enema" which scares people. I remember how I felt when I was presented with my first enema kit. Horrified. A bit scared! And thinking that it was downright unsavoury. Well let me reassure you that they're not as bad as you might think, in fact if I don't do my daily one, I really miss it.

I call it my daily crappocino. Which is why no-one invites me for a coffee any more!

How to do a coffee enema AKA having a Crappocino
You will need:-

- good quality organic coffee
- enema kit (I prefer the plastic bucket to the enema bags),
- towel
- timer
- comfortable place to lay on a waterproof pad or changing mat covered with towel or air bed if you're feeling delicate
- pillow

First make the coffee with filtered water, enough to fill the enema bucket (1 litre).

Run coffee through the tube to clear any bubbles and close valve.

The coffee needs to be at a comfortable temperature, test with your finger. If necessary, cool it with cold filtered water or ice cubes.

Get comfortable, laying on your back, insert the

nozzle you know where, using lubrication such as Vaseline or coconut oil if needed. Open the valve to release the coffee into your body. Hold or attach the bucket to a hook above you so that the coffee empties through the tube.

Once the coffee has all been taken into the body, close the valve and remove the nozzle. (You may find when you first start enemas, that you can't take the full litre comfortably. Don't worry, this will become easier with practice, so just take what is comfortable and build from there).

Lay on your right hand side for 12-20 minutes before using the toilet and releasing the coffee.

Thoroughly clean the kit and leave to dry. Keep some kitchen roll and eco-friendly cleaner at the side of the loo to have a quick clean up when you've finished.

At bedtime use a liver compress by putting a damp cloth over your liver (you know where it is don't you? On the right hand side just under your breast) and then placing a hot water bottle over it.

There are certain herbal remedies which support the liver such as milk thistle, and also some foods such as beetroot. I usually include beetroot in my daily juice every other day.

Periodically, say a couple of times a year, you can do a full liver cleanse. It is believed to be particularly effective at the time of a full moon. These dates are usually indicated in your diary with a full moon symbol, which comes around once a month. I did a full week version when I was at the 3E Centre which was quite hard core, and you need to clear your diary to do this. You may feel a bit delicate – I certainly did. But at the end of it I passed hundreds of stones! Better out than in, my mum used to say. There is a two day liver cleanse in one of the books I recommend; "Everything You Need to Know to Help you Beat Cancer" by Chris Woolams, which is a lot easier to fit in with your life, so this is the one I use nowadays, and it's pretty effective.

Liver Cleanse
Ingredients
½ cup extra virgin olive oil
1 very big grapefruit (providing ¾ cup of juice)
4 tablespoons of Epsom Salts
3 cups of water
Ornithine tablets

Preparation
Set aside three days

Day 1

Eat a no-fat breakfast and lunch

Eat and drink nothing after 2.00pm

Mix the Epsom Salts in the water (easier if the water is warm), then cool

6.00pm Drink a quarter of this liquid

8.00pm Drink a further quarter of the liquid

10.00pm Mix the olive oil and pulp-free grapefruit juice and shake vigorously. Drink the liquid through a straw before 10.15pm Take four ornithine tablets to help you sleep. Retire immediately and massage your stomach. Focus your mind on your liver and imagine the toxins leaving it, along with the stones. Sleep.

Day 2

Upon waking and not before 7.00am take the third quarter of the Epsom Salts mix. Two hours later take the last quarter.

Expect diarrhoea for two days. Don't eat before lunch time on day two and keep food to salads and fruit, plus baked potatoes for days two and three. You may need to repeat this treatment after a few weeks.

Skin

Your skin is the largest organ in the human body. One third of your body's toxins are excreted through the skin.

Dry brushing helps to unclog pores, therefore improving the excretion of toxins by the skin. It also stimulates your lymphatic system. Before bathing, using a skin brush or loofah, brush the legs, then arms and torso vigorously towards the heart. Hop in the shower to rinse. Then bathe in 100g of bicarbonate of soda for 30-45 mins to draw out the toxins.

Saunas are great to draw impurities out through the pores.

Colon

The immune system relies on a healthy colon. A clean high-fibre diet is important (see chapter 8). Over the years there can be accumulations in the colon which are stagnant and toxic. I had 10 colonic hydrotherapy treatments over 5 weeks whilst I was at the 3E Centre, and even on the 10th treatment there was a surprising amount of gunk coming out of there! (I know, too much information). The proper term for this is "impacted fecal matter". Ugh. I think that "better out than in" phrase is appropriate. This fecal matter becomes toxic, which is absorbed into the bloodstream, affecting the body's ability to metabolise food properly.

I recommend that anyone undertaking a wellness programme considers colonic hydrotherapy. You can find a therapist at www.colonic-association.org.

Lungs

Our breathing tends to be quite shallow, when we should be breathing in and out much more deeply in order to get the right levels of oxygen into the system.

Try doing some deep breathing when you are out in the fresh air or at an open window if you can't be outside.

- Breathe in through your nose to a count of 8, expanding your chest,
- Hold for a count of 8, and then breathe out, blowing through your mouth and making a noise so that you really empty your lungs.

If you need help, some therapies are really helpful at improving your breathing such as yoga, and shiatsu massage.

Lymphatic system

The lymphatic system is a network of tubes throughout the body that drains fluid (called lymph) from tissues and empties it back into the bloodstream. The main roles of the lymphatic system include managing the fluid levels in the body, filtering out bacteria, and housing types of white blood cells. Lymph is filtered through the spleen, thymus and lymph nodes before being emptied into the blood. It is a vital part of the immune system.

The lymphatic system is a bit like your veins but they don't have the heart as a pump so we have to help it to circulate and not stagnate. The best way of doing this is movement. I use a mini trampoline for 5 – 10 minutes a day. It's fun too! It makes me feel like a kid again.

I also have had Manual Lymphatic Drainage (MLD) massage, but you do need to consult your therapist before proceeding with this is you have cancer. There is a worry that it will spread the cancer. In my case we decided to go ahead because of the other treatments I was taking to boost my immune system.

Skin brushing is also great for stimulating the lymphatic system.

Kidneys
The kidneys regulate water and remove wastes from the body. The best thing we can do to help the kidneys is to drink plenty of osmosis or carbon filtered water.

The mouth
Oral health is an important indicator for overall health so is more important than we think. It can affect, or be affected by, or contribute to various diseases and conditions, such as cardiovascular disease.

- Dentistry – some believe that root canal work is linked to cancer. Amalgam fillings are 50% mercury. Avoid having these in future. If you have already had the work done, do not disturb them by having them taken out if you have cancer. If this is an issue for you, consult a holistic dentist.

- Oil pulling – aka Swish and Go This is an ancient Ayurvedic practice to clear bacteria, organisms, and metals from the mouth. I guarantee that you will not have bleeding gums if you do this every morning.

How to Swish and Go

You need – cold pressed organic oil in glass bottle (sunflower, sesame, olive or coconut), tablespoon, and paper-cup.

Take one tablespoon of the cold pressed organic oil into your mouth and really work and swish it around the mouth, teeth, gums and cheeks for 10-15 mins before spitting it out into the cup. (Not into the sink, if you do this every morning you will have plumbing problems to contend with!)

The oil mixes with the saliva, turning it into a thin white watery liquid. Lipids in the oils begin to pull out toxins from the saliva. As the oil is swished around the mouth, teeth, gums and

---

tongue, the oil continues to absorb the toxins turning thick and white. Once the oil has reached this consistency, spit it out before the toxins are re-absorbed.

One of my latest discoveries which really helped my detoxing efforts is bioresonance. Firstly it can be used as a diagnostic tool. And it can also be used to clear a whole host of nasties – in my case it cleared liver flukes, candida, Rife virus, heavy metals, and traces of chemotherapy and the contraceptive pill to name but a few. All of this by a non-invasive treatment with no side effects. It's absolutely fascinating!

David Franklin is the therapist who treated me, and is the distributor of the BICOM bioresonance equipment here in the UK. He has a vast amount of experience of treating people with this therapy, and here he tells us a bit more:-

Introduction to bioresonance
"The Oxford dictionary describes "resonance" as - "The condition in which an object or system is subjected to an oscillating force having a frequency close to its own natural frequency." That sounds a bit complicated, but it's easy to illustrate with a tuning fork and a piano string. When a tuning fork is tapped the piano string that has a matching frequency starts to oscillate. This

appears to be magic but it's just frequency patterns being passed through the air from one object to the next. We all know that some Opera singers can shatter a wine glass with their voices, this is achieved when the pitch the voice matches that of the wine glass structure. In both instances, when there is a reaction by the host, resonance occurs.

Bioresonance therefore is resonance between biological substances - that is living matter. This is mainly used in bioenergetics medicine. But to understand how that works we need to know some facts about living matter. What is matter? Albert Einstein discovered that matter is simply compressed energy, he even gave us a formula $E=mc2$. So each cell in the body including toxins, bacteria, parasites, viruses, and even tumours have energy patterns unique to themselves. Because of this understanding of our physical world it has become possible to record these frequency patterns, large databases of these have been built over the last 50 years. So here is the clever part:

Let's take E.Coli for example, this has a frequency pattern of 799-804 Khz so if a frequency generator transmitted this frequency to a person with E.Coli "resonance" would occur which can be recorded by a resonance machine. This can be used to "aid" diagnosis that can certainly speed up finding the root cause behind symptoms. We say "aid" because we are dealing with many frequencies emitted from the body and a clinical *observations are important too. The advantage for the patient is an understanding on why they are sick and what they can do to get better.*

Treatment by bioresonance

So we have a good idea what the problem might be, but we will only truly know if we are correct when we remove this problem and the patient starts to gets better. So how is this done? Well people get ill when their immune system becomes compromised, so therapists using a Bicom Optima device have been trained to support the patient before running elimination programs. Basic therapy followed by removing blockages, liver, lymph and kidney activation programs are essential.

So how can a pathogen be eliminated? It has been observed under a microscope that sending an inverted frequency pattern of a substance can break up the pathogens cellular structure, we observed this with the wine glass. This understanding is also used with noise cancelling headphone, tiny microphones are placed inside the headsets which pick up ambient noise; this can be up to 70 decibels on a plane. The headphones then send an inverted frequency which cancels out the noise enabling you to enjoy your music.

So it is possible for an electronic device to:-

1. Eliminate pathogens in the body or

2. Damage it which helps the immune system to fight it or

3. Awaken the immune systems, which then goes to work

This method is being used by thousands of doctors, veterinary surgeons and therapists worldwide, but will it ever become mainstream? Will funding ever be found to verify this scientifically? As you may already know, if it cannot be patented then there is no commercial interest and therefore many efforts have been made to suppress this information and keep it from the general populace. That's exactly what is happening to natural remedies that have been curing various ailments without harmful side effects for thousands of years. More information can be found at www.reson8.co.uk.

Cancer Quest

In the 1920's a US scientist and inventor Raymond Rife developed a microscope that allowed him to observe bacteria. Electron microscopes kill the specimens. He discovered that bacteria could change its form and become cancer causing viruses. When this virus was injected into rats tumours began to appear. The virus became known as Cryptocides Primordiales.

Rife then began to beam various light frequencies at the viruses and found that they appeared to disintegrate in the display of his microscope. When applied to the rats their tumours disappeared too. Human trials began under supervision of a university and medical doctor with confirmed success rates of over 90%. Unfortunately this research was covered up and the FDA still do not approve of treating patients with methods similar to Rife. Integrated medicine practitioners that use these light frequencies on this virus have had similar success but there is no silver bullet for cancer and other doctors have found other pathogens that they were convinced caused cancer. It is still important to look for and treat this virus for those looking to remove stress on the body and possible causes of cancer.

Dr Hulda Clark was another American doctor who found herself on the wrong side of the medical industry when she said in a number of her books that she had found the cure for cancer. Websites based on her research explain that a human liver fluke called Fasciolopsis buski work with other toxins to cause all malignancies.

Patients that have been prescribed herbal parasite cleanses or had bioresonance have sometimes noticed these in their toilet bowl following treatment and especially after a liver flush. Liver flushes uses Epsom salts, olive oil and citrus juice which when taken in a certain way which relaxes and squeezes the bile ducts which produces a flood of bile which can push out stones and parasites with them. Removing these stressors to the body is an essential part of restoring health to the patient.

Dr Tullio Simoncini from Italy is an Oncologist who is convinced that Candida is actually cancer and has injected 1000's of patients with bicarbonate of soda directly on the tumours. This causes them to disintegrate, the success of his treatments have been observed for over 20 years and still being used today.

Because the Cancer Act will not permit non oncologists to treat cancer many have avoided even repeating the above controversial forms of treatment. However it is possible to be treated for Candida, viruses and parasites easily and without harming the body, in fact it's an important start to restore health for most known conditions. When these and other health regimes mentioned in this book are used some have discovered that the body begins to heal itself.

Conventional medicine usually does not look for these factors and actually promotes diets during chemotherapy that can encourage the growth of candida and cancer. A good bioresonance therapist can find these stressors and help the body eliminate them.

For a list of these worldwide please visit www. bioresonance.institute".

David Franklin
BiocomUK
www.reson8.uk.com.

I hope that this gives you some ideas on how you can reduce the toxic load in your body. You can easily build these into your regular routine.

CHAPTER 7 – THE YUMSCIOUS NUTRITION PLAN

Let food by thy medicine and medicine be thy food
Hippocrates, father of medicine 431 B.C.

Clever chap that Hippocrates. Even way back then he knew that food was all about nutrition and helping the body to do its job. This way of thinking seems to have been somewhat lost on many 21st Century eating habits: We eat as a treat, because it's meal-time, to be sociable, to provide comfort or to alleviate boredom. Hippocrates promoted a healthy lifestyle, moderation, cleanliness and exercise. The other thing he is well known for, even now, is the Hippocratic Oath taken by doctors. The Oath which says "first do no harm", which I always think is interesting when you consider chemotherapy as a treatment. I digress – back to food.

Think of your body as a machine (a diesel car perhaps) and then imagine what would happen to it if you filled it with petrol. (Or maybe you already know what happens from experience – like me. Oops!). It isn't pretty. The car cannot keep going, splutters and conks out. Our bodies were designed to consume lots of natural foods, yet we now insist on feeding it with processed and packaged foods which it is not able to digest. This causes stress on the body as it uses unnecessary energy to try to do so. In some cases, it too splutters and conks out. This may show up as food intolerances or allergies, or become a contributory factor to a more serious illness.

We seem to have a pre-occupation with diet and dieting in our society don't we? We are always looking for the next 'High-diet-this' or 'Low-plan-that' to follow. I am not intending to be so absolutely prescriptive here. I will, however, provide some information for you so that you understand what the best choices are for your health.

What needs doing is to get back in touch with your body, with your appetite, and what your body needs to function, keep well and heal. When it's time to eat, ask yourself if you are really hungry, rather than eating for any other reason. Make sure you're hydrated – don't confuse thirst for hunger.

If you are hungry, the question to ask yourself is "what nutrition does my body need right now". I guarantee that if you do this, and tap into how your body feels, and what impact the food you eat has on your body, you will make better choices.

In my five weeks at the 3E Centre, I learned the Budwig diet protocol. Remember that they have studied cancer survivors around the world, and these are the resulting guidelines. Which is why I followed them to the absolute letter on my return home.

The Budwig Oil-Protein Diet

One of the key parts of the protocol is the Oil-Protein or quark and oil mixture, which was discovered by Dr Johanna Budwig. She was a qualified pharmacist, a chemist with a doctorate in chemistry and physics, and later studied medicine. She was nominated for a Nobel prize seven times – so we are talking about a big hitter here. She understood the healing powers of Omega 3, and Omega 6, fatty acids and the dangers of hydrogenated oils. Through this research came the Oil-Protein diet which brings energy back to the cells.

A healthy cell makes energy using oxygen. Cancer cells are abnormal, and when not getting enough oxygen use fermentation to survive. So getting more oxygen into cells is important. Inflammation is a main component of cancer's metastatic process – this mixture contains powerful anti-inflammatory substances. This is not a science book, so that is my very simple interpretation of what it does. The full explanation is complex and far too scientific for me I'm afraid. If you're interested to learn more about the science, I can recommend the book "A Day in the Budwig Diet" by Ursula Escher and Gene Wei.

Recommended consumption of the quark and oil mixture is 5g per kg of weight. For example, if you weigh 60kg, you need to eat 300g of quark per day.

Here are the key principles of the Budwig Oil-Protein diet plan -

DO's
• Use fresh, organic, good quality foods wherever possible
• Drink freshly made juices to increase intake of vitamins and nutrients
• Eat quark and oil mixture during the day as dessert or salad dressing
• Avoid sugar – in cakes, biscuits etc., also in high sugar fruits such as bananas. Ideally 1 banana per week maximum
• Make your own salad dressings using cold-pressed organic oils in glass bottles such as sunflower or olive oil
• Eat quark and oil every day – 5g per kg of weight. E.g. if you weigh 60kg, have 300g of quark during the day
• For cooking, only use hard coconut oil
• Control carbohydrate consumption – potatoes once a week, pasta once a month maximum
• Limit dairy products, use milk substitutes such as almond, coconut or oat milk
• Drink lots of filtered water, green or herbal teas
• Eat a rainbow of coloured foods on your plate to make sure you are getting a wide range of nutrients
• Learn about veggie and vegan food and how to make it tasty and interesting
• Look after your gut health, with fermented foods such as sauerkraut or buttermilk
• Eat unsalted unprocessed nuts

DON'T's
• Eat meat, fish or eggs
• Eat packaged and processed foods including bread
• Eat anything with a face or a mother
• Avoid trans-fats e.g. margarine, instant noodles, fast food, cup-a-soups etc.
• Avoid alcohol if there are any problems with the liver. Otherwise an occasional glass of champagne or red wine is fine. (God bless Johanna)
• Avoid soya products
• Avoid peanuts

Let's look at how that looks on a daily basis, what will you actually be eating, and when:-

The daily Budwig nutrition plan

- The first thing you should consume on waking and on an empty stomach, is a drink of Sauerkraut juice. Fermented foods are brilliant for gut health. You can make this yourself, or it can be obtained by mail order from The German Deli in London www. germandeli.co.uk If you can't face it (it is a bit of an acquired taste) have buttermilk, or a good quality probiotic

- Breakfast should be the quark and oil mixture with fruit, and linomel (see Recipes)

- Mid-morning – first juice of the day. Carrot or beetroot. (See Recipes)

- Lunch-
  - salad starter with raw vegetables (eg carrots, radish, kohlrabi, cauliflower), green salads, and fresh herbs served with "Budwig mayonnaise" (see Recipes)
  - warm vegetarian meal eg steamed vegetables with oleolux (see Recipes), buckwheat, millet flavoured with fresh herbs. Occasionally potatoes (once a week) or rice (twice a month)
  - dessert – quark and oil mixture with fruit and flavourings such as lemon, vanilla, coconut
- Mid-afternoon – second juice, grape, papaya or pineapple. (All of which have enzymes helpful to those with cancer. Can be bought if it's packaged in glass bottles, and organic.)
- Evening meal (ideally no later than 6.00pm) – Salad selection, rice cakes and small amount of hard cheese such as Edam. Home-made soup.
- Snacks – nuts, seeds, fruit, quark and oil.
- Drinks – filtered water, herbal teas, green and white tea, occasional wine or champagne.

If you have cancer, or are facing a healing crisis, it's recommended that you follow this as closely as possible for up to 5 years. I followed this plan to the absolute letter when I returned home from the 3E Centre. I kept myself on a very tight rein and didn't deviate at all. It was very important to me to give it my best shot, and to give my body the very best chance I could for it to heal. But I don't think I got it quite right. I forgot that I also have a life to live, and that food and socialising are big pleasures in life. I turned down invitations if it meant eating after 6.00 p.m. as the regime came first.

Regime being the operative word. Thus, my social life, and therefore seeing friends, lost out. But as we have already learned, happiness and connecting with others are extremely important parts of wellness too. So I have adapted the plan slightly to suit me, so that I enjoy it more, and it's therefore sustainable over time.

Here is how I have amended what I do. I missed eggs! I decided I didn't want to live in a world without omelettes. So I now buy organic free range eggs and omelettes are back on the menu. I generally eat at 6ish when I'm at home, but if I'm invited out for dinner, I go. When I am out, veggie dishes are not always the healthiest option. So I might say no to the pastry-laden veggie dish, and yes to organic, farm-fed chicken if that's what I think I will really enjoy. Or I might ask the chef to make me the most interesting salad he's ever made, or an alternative healthy veggie dish. They are always more than happy to oblige – I think they like the challenge.

People often asked me how I could keep it going; such a strict plan.

Firstly, it's absolutely not about willpower. Willpower only lasts so long before it runs out. It's more about choice – choice-power. What do you choose for your health, and your body? Remember what I said at the beginning - don't ask yourself "what do I fancy to eat?" That is asking your taste buds, and they are addicted to sugar and processed foods. Instead, ask every cell in your body what it needs, and tap into that. Really savour and enjoy your choices. The smell and texture and visual impact of fresh fruit and vegetables is amazing. Think of a ripe nectarine, or juicy melon, or a tasty crunchy salad. Treat yourself to some fresh asparagus, or a beautiful avocado. Enjoy preparing it for yourself. Put some love in it. Eat it slowly and consciously, imagine the nourishment finding its way to your cells, and feel cherished and looked after.

How lovely does that all sound?

And the final thing I've learned is – chill out. Do your best, but don't stress about it. So long as you eat and drink well most of the time your overall health will improve.

Tasty Tips

1. find a local farm shop for fresh organic veggies
2. try a new fruit or vegetable every week
3. prepare your food with love
4. have a rainbow of colours on your plate
5. eat consciously, savouring the taste and texture
6. eat when you're hungry
7. learn what your body needs
8. get a great veggie cookbook
9. learn about alkaline foods and eat more of them
10. make food and nutrition a priority.

Gadgets and gizmos – to make your life easier

Juicer – don't put it away in a cupboard, you will be using it every single day of your life!

Coffee grinder- to make Linomel

Mandolin- makes veggies and salads much prettier. Mind your fingers though!

Salad saver - so that your salad keeps fresh for as long as possible in the fridge

Soup maker - delicious home-made soup in 20 mins and as easy as boiling the kettle

RECIPES

QUARK AND OIL

Firstly, you need to get your provisions, so here's your shopping list:-

quark - 250g tub of Golden Acre quark (sold in Asda and Waitrose). Suggest using half of it for one serving

oil - needs to be organic, cold pressed, in a dark glass bottle NOT plastic. I suggest you look in health food shops, I use one by Granovita. Use 2-3 tablespoons for one serving

milk - non-dairy e.g. coconut or almond
fresh fruit

ground flax seeds (linomel)

pineapple juice or honey to sweeten

nuts, cinnamon, vanilla extract, coconut or cocoa powder to flavour

To make - put half a tub of quark into a bowl. Measure 3 tablespoons of flax oil, and use a fork to blend the oil into the quark. You may need to use a small amount of milk for the oil to be absorbed into the mixture and have a smooth texture.

From here, you can go freelance and do whatever

your taste buds fancy. You need to use something to sweeten the mix - honey for example. I use this only occasionally as cancer feeds on sugar. I prefer to use a fruit juice, such as pineapple juice. Although it has sugars in it, it's not as sweet as honey and the enzymes are helpful. You can include fresh fruit - my favourites are blueberries for breakfast, and strawberries if eating it as dessert. I also like a cheeky little pineapple juice/coconut combo – a bit like a Piña Colada in a bowl. If I feel really decadent, I might use a small amount of cocoa powder with fresh orange or strawberries. Yum.

Any of these mixtures can be popped into the freezer so that you have an ice cream effect. I sometimes do this with quark/milk/vanilla extract, and then have it with a baked apple.

See - I still know how to live on the edge.

I eat a version of this for breakfast, and for dessert after lunch.

It can also be flavoured with herbs, garlic etc., and used as a salad dressing or dip.

LINOMEL

This cereal was created by Dr. Budwig, and can be added to your breakfast quark and oil, to juices wine or champagne.

You need to use a ratio of 6 to 1 of flaxseeds to honey. Flaxseeds are also known as linseeds.

- 6 teaspoons of whole flax seeds
- 1 teaspoon of pure local honey

Use a coffee grinder to grind the flax seeds for approx. 5 seconds. You are aiming for them to be cracked to aid digestion, not to be a powder. Next, add the honey. This is to protect the grounded seeds from oxidation. Ideally make it fresh each day, but it can be stored in the fridge for 3-4 days.

OLEOLUX

This is Dr Budwig's healthy alternative to butter. It's delicious over vegetables, and can add flavour to soups and salad dressings.

You need
- 125ml of very cold flax seed oil
- 250g of solid coconut oil
- 1 medium onion
- 10 garlic cloves

Start by putting the flax oil in the freezer. Let it cool for about 30 mins.

Add the coconut fat and a half-cut onion into a frying pan. Cook for approx. 15 mins. Add the garlic cloves and heat for an extra 3 to 5 minutes.

Put the now cold flax seed oil into a mixing bowl. Use a strainer to strain the coconut oil mixture into the bowl. Mix well and refrigerate. It has a long shelf life of approx. 4 months, or 1 year if frozen.

BUDWIG MAYONNAISE
Mix two soup spoons of flax/linseed oil with 2 soup spoons of milk and 2 soup spoons of quark in a blender. Add 2 soup spoons of lemon juice or cider vinegar and with 1 teaspoon of mustard and fresh herbs

JUICES
Here are some recipes to get you started, but feel free to add whatever you have in the fridge. You might need to have more fruit to sweeten the juices until you get a taste for it, when you can then add more vegetables than fruit.

Zingtastic (have on alternate days)

3 carrots, 2 apples, ½ lime peeled, chunk of ginger (all organic or well washed)

Put the carrots into the juicer, followed by the lime and ginger, topped with the apples. Serve with ice. Deeeelicious.

Ravishing Red Juice (have on alternate days)

2 raw beetroot, 2-3 apples, 2 sticks celery, chunk of cucumber, ginger to taste, ½ lime peeled (all organic or well-washed)

Put the beetroot in first, followed by the ginger and lime, apples and finally celery and cucumber. I like it served on ice. Please note – how can I put this – when you next go to the toilet you will think that you are bleeding to death, but it's just the beetroot working through your system, so panic not.

Green Goodness

Green juices are wonderfully alkaline for the body. Use whatever greens you have in the fridge, such as kale, Brussel sprouts, cabbage, romaine lettuce, broccoli, and asparagus. To make more palatable, mix in a small amount of fruit such as apples, pears, or pineapple. Use lime and/or ginger if you like. I do. Always.

Juice everything, serve over ice. Drink, and smile thinking of how happy all your cells are.

Chapter 8 – THE WOO-WOO STUFF

Why do I call it the woo-woo stuff? Well in the days of 'pre-breast cancer' that is exactly what I thought of all this. It wasn't an informed opinion by the way. Just that I thought it was for bohemian-types and wasn't really in my consciousness.

I now know differently, especially as I was facing such a serious situation and I became open to what I learned. And I learned that people who survive cancer do many of these things to look after themselves.

So who was I to argue?

Don't underestimate the power of the therapy itself. But there is more to it than that. In my experience, the people who are drawn to making a living in this way are very special people. So not only do you get the therapy itself, but you get the care and experience of a therapist who has chosen to do this, in many instances, as a calling. Who has real love for their craft, and for YOU? Wow. It's hardly surprising that it works. We know how powerful LOVE is - don't we?

So, what therapies am I talking about? There are many to choose from. In some ways, I don't think it matters which ones you choose. If you are drawn to a particular therapy, then I would say trust your instinct as that is probably the best choice for you. I have tended to look for the people I was drawn to, the ones who seemed to appear in my path. It's my belief that the universe helps you to find what, and who, you are meant to find, and that has certainly been the case for me.

I met Kimm, a most wonderful healer and amazing human being, before I was diagnosed, so it was easy to turn to her when I needed to. I found a Bowen therapist through twitter. I found a herbalist and shiatsu practitioner through The Haven breast cancer charity. I found my Journey Therapist after reading Brandon Bay's book, which was recommended to me by the 3E Centre. Bioresonance was recommended to me by a fellow breast cancer survivor, whose opinion I really value. This is my preferred approach, as the people aspect is so important.

I also make sure that I listen to my body, and respond to what it needs. At the times I have been most anxious (when waiting for scan results, or after difficult discussions with the doc) I seem to store a huge amount of tension in my neck and shoulders. At those times, my therapy budget would be spent to alleviate that – Bowen, or physio, or massage.

On the other hand, if you have always been fascinated by acupuncture, or homeopathy, do that. But take a bit of time to find the right therapist to work with.

I like variety, and I love to try new things, so I mix it

up. In the last 2 ½ years I have tried one thing, and then moved on to another. Or if it's something that you enjoy, and feel it is helping you on an ongoing basis, keep it as a constant. Some of my constants are healing, mindfulness and bioresonance.

Here are some of the therapies I have experienced:-
- Reiki
- Healing and chakra balancing
- Herbal medicine
- Shiatsu massage
- Bowen
- Manual Lymphatic Drainage massage
- Bioresonance
- The Journey therapy
- Cranio-sacral therapy
- Physiotherapy
- Oxygen therapy

And these are the therapies I can do for myself at home:-
- Infrared Heat lamp
- Liver compress
- Mindfulness
- Emotional freedom technique (EFT), also known as tapping.

You need to choose the therapies which you feel will increase your wellbeing, and support your body and immune system to do its job. That will reduce inflammation or toxicity in the body.

Be curious. Ask others, especially DIBs what they recommend. Mix it up.

SUPPLEMENTS

Every day I take a huge number of pills and potions. This has been under the guidance of the 3E Centre initially, and now working with Cancer Options. The list has changed over time – as referenced above I like variety, and I like to mix it up. Cancer adapts, and I want to keep it on its toes!

I believe that these supplements/treatments have made a huge difference in keeping me well. It's difficult to prove that statement. We don't have the luxury of trying one thing at a time, so that we can categorically know what is making the difference. But comparing myself to others I see with a similar diagnosis, or undertaking similar treatments is enough to convince me that I am doing the right things.

I have decided not to give a definitive list of the supplements I take – because as described above it changes. Also, what is right for me, at this particular point in time, is unlikely to be right for you. There are some amazing resources out there to help you devise your own plan. As you know, I would recommend working under the guidance of an expert such as Patricia Peat. If you want to go freelance, then the CancerActive website (www.canceractive.com) has all the information you could possibly need.

Broadly speaking, these supplements aim to get your body in a position to heal itself - boosting your immune system, using known cancer-fighting compounds, getting your body back in balance and harmony.

As these therapies and supplements have been such a significant part of my healing, I have asked a couple of the people I've worked with to give more information on their particular area of expertise.

Bowen and MLD - Dr Alison Merrick

"I am now an independent therapist working with people using Bowen Therapy and MLD (Manual Lymphatic Drainage) and I have a special interest in cancer.

Why?

Well I worked for 10 years in Cancer Research at St James's in Leeds developing new therapies using the immune system to overcome cancer. I worked with a lot of oncologists and specialist nurses who were doing wonderful work within their field. Over time though, it became obvious to me that there were gaping holes in the care we were giving people.

All the consultants admitted it was normal to have to prescribe anti-depressants. Yes people would also have problems sleeping (more pills), financial worries (refer to social services), eating (just eat what you like) the list goes on. But that was outside their remit, and the occasional 'Quality of Life' studies run in the clinics, were a bit woolly and irrelevant. Everything was centred on finding the right drug, radiotherapy schedule and surgery to eliminate the cancer in a more focussed way. Focussed, or blinkered? It has been said many times before but the 'person' was not treated, the cancer was treated and the person was almost ignored. Oncologists are not taught to treat the whole person.

What makes us whole? And what makes us a healthy whole? I see a few areas of importance. Our emotional and mental health affects everything. We all know that we feel happier when the sun shines and our pain is worse when we feel down. We now have sound research showing that stress and negativity directly affect our physiology and can CAUSE disease. It doesn't mean that it is easy to remain forever positive, but it does mean that doing all we can to help ourselves to keep stress free and as positive as we can, is essential for our health.

Nutrition has to play a major role in our health. I'm not a nutritionist, but obviously we need to give our bodies' quality nourishment to thrive. This is getting more difficult with depleted soils and a decrease in our food quality. A good varied and unadulterated diet using organic ingredients whenever possible must be the best way to support good body function. Additionally, good quality herbals/supplements can help enormously, especially in illness.

Physical health and taking care of our bodies, including everything from exercise to minimising our exposure to unnecessary external stressors, chemicals and pollutants.

There is a real need in this country to move towards more integrative medicine. We are lagging behind! I left my research career and retrained as a 'remedial' therapist, it sounds like a cliché but I wanted to make a difference to people. I do refer to and have referrals from other therapists and although we all work independently we form our own networks. Ideally I would love to see integrated clinics where multiple therapies can be available under one roof. I think, I hope this will come in the future.

So what do I do?

Bowen is a very gentle and balancing therapy. It can help all kinds of aches and pains, and is very useful at all parts of the cancer journey. It has no contra-indications, can be used even when people are feeling very poorly, and they can be sitting, lying or even standing to receive it. People have it before, during or after chemo and/or radiotherapy to relax and reduce side effects. The main 'side effect' of Bowen is to improve sleep patterns and help energy levels. People will often remark that they feel 'more themselves', 'more balanced' and generally calmer. Pain medication is often reduced and digestive problems settle. In the medium and long term, people come back for a 'top-up' to maintain balance.

MLD or Manual Lymphatic Drainage (it sounds dreadful but it really isn't!). This is actually a clinical therapy that is used in the NHS for the management of lymphoedema, and that is a part of what I do. But in other countries it is used much more broadly. It is an amazing massage that moves the lymphatic fluid around the body much more quickly than it ever does normally. So it is like using a power hose to clean everything out. It will clear congestion and toxins that have been sitting around in tissues (including the liver) and lymph nodes for years, even decades. This is really important in metabolising and clearing drugs and anaesthetics, and also allows the immune system and all the bodies healing mechanisms to work much more effectively. It brings better rhythm to the digestive system and recent studies have shown that it directly affects heart rate, blood pressure and brain waves, interrupts pain signals and brings deep relaxation.

If you would like to find out more then please contact me."

e: alison@dralisonmerrick.co.uk
w: dralisonmerrick.co.uk
m: 07805 644125
Clinics at Skipton, Keighley and Saltaire in West Yorkshire.

The Journey – Anne Winslow

"As technology has advanced so rapidly in recent years and things beyond our wildest dreams are now possible with computers, phones etc., it is apparent that when it comes to our health we are still lacking in progress, particularly cancer. This has opened the door to more and more people looking to a holistic approach and actually getting amazing results.

I believe that there is a wisdom within us that will guide us and show us the way in life, we just need to connect to it, and listen to it! With Journey Therapy you access that wise part of yourself and look to healing all the hurts and wounds that we pick up in life. It can be an emptying out of the old and no longer needed and empowering of the present. It's also a great place to talk to parts of your body, ask how you can help, you can even talk to the cancer and ask what needs to happen for it to leave. Within that space you can send healing energy to your body too.

There may be specific incidents that you know need healing from the past or it could just be about connecting to a wonderful relaxing space, a place of deep love beyond your imagination and letting it guide you. The great thing is whatever happens within an appointment it is controlled by the 'wise' part of you, so you are always in control. It is exactly what is right for you.

My intention when working with every client is that

they access their own inner wisdom, the love, light and healing energy that exists within and allow the root cause of all the issues to be healed and released in the gentlest most beneficial way.

People often say they feel lighter after an appointment, like a weight has been lifted from them. They feel more empowered and their intuition is heightened, feeling more in control and knowing what is right for them.

I feel honoured to have played a small part in Nina's healing Journey. When Nina came to see me she was already well into her healing programme, but needed a boost. I always ask a client what they want to achieve from an appointment, to think of an intention, like goal setting at a deeper level. You would imagine that someone coming to see you with Stage 4 cancer would say I want to be healed, but never presume.

Nina's intention was to get her strength, belief and confidence back, that she could do this. And if dreams come true, to find a life-partner.

Nina's process was very beautiful, accessing a quiet reflective place to stop, think and chat. A lot of wisdom and understanding was gained there, and things to do to help her body heal. Nina also connected to herself at a younger age, and had a powerful conversation. She then went on to heal old relationships, then connect with the cancer, and scanned her whole body, gaining wisdom and understanding. Nina described it as a very positive experience.

I was excited to meet up with Nina several months later when she came to give a talk to the '100 Inspiring Women' group in Grimsby. She looked radiant. It was great to share her intention, and how she had found her strength, belief and confidence and was using techniques that had come to her during the process. I was also thrilled to hear that there was a man her life too. Always best to ask for exactly what you want.

I would say dare to try something different, most therapies can run alongside conventional treatment or stand alone, whichever is your preference. There is a wise loving space within you just waiting for you to connect with it, so it can guide you step by step along your journey. The right people will come along, you will hear about different things, and have an inner knowing which direction to take.

I wish you love and blessings on your journey."

Anne Winslow x Quest Therapies 07757 26 30 26 E-mail anne@quest-therapies.com Facebook www.facebook.com/journeytherapy Website www.quest-therapies.com

****

These are just two examples of the many therapies I have used. They form a crucial part of the self-nurturing approach to wellness, and I have enjoyed trying different things and had the privilege of meeting some wonderful, caring people.

CHAPTER 9 – YOUR VERY OWN CANCER MAVERICK 'LOVE YOURSELF BETTER' PLAN

This is a really important chapter because this is not a book that you can just read and then put back on the shelf. If you do that, lack of action means that it's not going to work in any way at all.

If you have cancer, you need to make sure that you DO SOMETHING. And then you keep on doing something, every single day, most probably for the rest of your life.

I do hope that doesn't sound too daunting – it's not meant to. Remember that most of the things you need to do are enjoyable, they are all about self-care, and self-love. Investing time and money in taking care of yourself. Please don't think that is being selfish. Very much the opposite. It is only by looking after yourself that you have the energy and resources to look after others. You will be around longer to love and care for the other people in your life.

If you don't have cancer, but are looking to stay healthy, the same applies – you need to DO SOMETHING.

Let's get going:-

1. Decide what it is that you want to do.

How do you know? When you are dealing with a dire cancer diagnosis, these decisions feel very hard. They can literally be a matter of 'life and death'. No pressure then! Hopefully this book has given you lots of ideas and pointers. But only you know what the real issues are for you. That pause button will give you the time and space to figure it out. Your doses of Vitamin P mean that you are in the right frame of mind. Listen to yourself. Trust yourself. Tap into where it is that you feel whether your decisions are good ones. It might be your head, your heart, or your gut. For me it's definitely gut. If I decide to do something and I feel sick, then I know it's not the right decision.

Whatever you're thinking of doing, try it on for size. Imagine doing it, visualise. Remember that your brain doesn't know the difference between imagination and reality, so it really is a worthwhile exercise. This can be especially helpful if you are considering a choice which is seen as unconventional. Like a mental "try before you buy".

If you have worked through (and I really do mean worked) the previous chapters, you will be ready to decide. If you're not, then you can always go back and work through your uncertainties. Even though the stakes are high, don't get too stressed.

Doing something will always take you towards your goal, even if you learn that it's not the right thing. If you decide it's the wrong thing, it will help you know what to do next, what needs amending. You can go round the loop again if you need to.

2. Get excited!

Remember it's not a fight or battle, but an adventure. Accept the things you can't change, and concentrate on the things that you can – of which there will be many.

Be confident! The human spirit can conquer many situations. The human body is amazing, much cleverer than anything man can make artificially.

3. It's down to you.

The person in charge of your health is YOU. Take control. Take responsibility. Take action.

4. Your plan needs to cover all the following elements.

- The first E – Energie, or Mind and Spirit
- The second E – Eliminieren, or Eliminating toxins
- The third E – Essen, or Nutrition
- Your treatment plan and supplements
- Therapies and treatments

To help you to keep on track, there are some downloadable planners available by scanning the QR code below.

1. A typical day in the life of Nina Joy
2. Another to plot out your year – A whole year of Love and Adventure
3. A weekly planner – Love yourself better this week
4. A daily planner – Love yourself better today

These are to help you to -
    Keep the plan going
    Keep focused
    Enjoy it
    Make it fun

Or go to: www.ninajoy.com/index.php/downloads.

Love Yourself Better Today

This daily plan is to help you to pack all the things you want to do on a daily basis – enjoying some Vitamin P, looking after your state of mind, keeping your toxic load down, your nutrition up.

I have done an example of mine to give you some ideas how to use it.

Love Yourself Better This Week

There are some things that need doing on a weekly basis to keep you on track, such as shopping for organic food and supplies (online makes it easier), planning your menus, appointments for treatments or therapies. You may also want to plan in some activities to pursue your Bucket List.

A Whole Year of Love

This will help you keep tabs over a longer time frame, for example you may want to review your supplements regime 2 or 3 times a year, plan holidays or retreats, or Bucket List or Vision Board adventures.

As you have worked through this book, you will know what the right course of action is for YOU.

Tap into your gut instinct, or intuition. Some people

dismiss gut instinct but I believe it's really important. You know what's best for you. You need to make space to consider what you think, and to listen to your gut. Gut instinct is based on thousands of years of evolution, and many years of your own experience. So don't be afraid to trust it. How many times have you done something that's gone wrong, and said to yourself afterwards; "I knew that wasn't a good idea?" Many times I bet. That's because we instinctively know more than we give ourselves credit for.

Trust yourself. And then have the courage to act on it. Stick to your guns even if others don't agree with your decision. It's your life and your health. Try it on for size. Imagine how it will feel to be doing treatments x, y and z. Remember that the brain doesn't know the difference between imagination and reality! Whatever you decide, try it on for size mentally, and see if it feels the right thing to do. You will know.

A word of advice once you have devised your Plan

Everything you do, every single activity included in your plan - tell your body what it is going on, be that healing or detoxification or vitamins and nutrition.

Do it all consciously.

Visualise what is happening to clear your cells/ reduce the tumours/boost your immune system.

The power of the mind is amazing (as discussed in Chapter 6) so make sure you harness its immense power in everything you do.

CHAPTER 10 – SILVER LININGS - THE ADVENTURE CONTINUES

Your life has changed. You've changed. Things will never be the same again.

Let's face it, you've been through a lot. You've been through the thing that we all dread – hearing the words "you've got cancer". You may, like me have been diagnosed with advanced cancer, and told that it's incurable. Or terminal.

You will have had painful tests and treatments. You may be in pain from the cancer itself, the treatments, or have other physical issues. You have to cope with ongoing test results, and scans. You will have had many hospital appointments, and may have had lengthy hospital stays. You may have been told that the cancer you thought had been cured has come back. Or you live in dread of that happening.

It's hardly surprising that you've changed. But let's not assume that it's a totally bad thing.

You will have learned things about yourself, and the people around you. You will have met and probably made friends with some amazing people, who you wouldn't have met in other circumstances. You will have new found respect for your body and health.

Think of your life as a beautiful glass vase, and that one day it gets dropped and smashed to pieces. If you try to put it together exactly as it was before, it will look odd and damaged. If, however, you used the pieces to make something new, such as a mosaic, it would look different than before, but every bit as beautiful.

Your life post-cancer is similar. If you try to put it back together as before, it too can seem broken. But if you accept what has happened, and rebuild anew, it means you will be more resilient and open to this new way of living.

This isn't just my opinion. Amongst breast cancer survivors, two-thirds say that their lives have actually changed for the better. The reasons given?

- It gives you a real wake-up call, so that you are forced to focus on what matters.
- It gives you a sharpened appreciation of the relationships you have.
- Living in the present makes you appreciate what you have in the here and now.
- As a survivor, this boosts your confidence and belief in yourself, your strength and your resources.

Once you have coped with or conquered cancer, there is very little in life that phases you. I think of myself as one of 'The Incurables' – complete with super-hero cape and undies outside my trousers. It makes me feel strong and powerful. And I do like a good outfit.

You may have heard of PTSD – Post Traumatic Stress Disorder. It's an anxiety disorder brought on by the occurrence of a traumatic event. This is most often talked about in relation to the military who have endured the horrors of war, but it's also relevant in a non-military environment, and some people with cancer have PTSD.

What is less well known is that there's also a condition described as Post Traumatic Growth (PTG). This refers to how adversity can often be a springboard to a new and more meaningful life, where you re-evaluate your priorities, deepen your relationships, and reach a new understanding of where you are.

As a member of the Professional Speaking Association, I am acutely aware of this. Many, many, speakers have personal stories of overcoming adversity, and being better/stronger/happier because of their experiences.

Typically 30-70% of survivors say that they have experienced positive changes of one form or another.

PTG challenges the traditional psychiatric view of trauma and changes how we think about trauma and how to treat it. It doesn't necessarily mean that you can be entirely free of the memories of what's happened, the grief or distress, but that your life is more meaningful in the light of what has happened.

It's not about wiping away history, but welcoming it and the changes it has brought.

If you are not yet at this stage, there are ways to stimulate Post Traumatic Growth, understanding the significance of the experiences we've had, how we view ourselves as survivors and thrivers. You know what I'm going to suggest now don't you? Yes – it's Journal time again!

Time to do some work.

Questions to explore:-
- Are there things I did to survive what happened that show I have strength that I didn't know I had?
- Are there ways I have found a different perspective on life and new opportunities?
- Are there ways in which my relationships with family and friends have been strengthened and deepened?
- Are there ways in which I have found a greater understanding of life and how to live it?
- Are there ways in which I find myself being more grateful for what I have and for those around me?

By noticing these things, we encourage it happening. So ask yourself these questions periodically to nurture growth.

Having recognised that you are this *new/different/ stronger/happier/more grateful* (delete as appropriate) person, you are now ready for the rest of your life.

I say this as someone with incurable cancer, who has already outlived my prognosis by about 2 years. I feel as though I am living on borrowed time. I don't take for granted that I will be here for ever, or that I will be as well as I am for ever. But whilst I am, then I sure want to pack as much in as I can. As and when my health changes, I can change my plans accordingly. But I don't intend to sit around waiting for it to happen.

It's time to look to the future.

There are two things I like to do

The first one is a 'Bucket List'. I recommend that everyone has a Bucket List. Traditionally, this is done when you're dying. Frankly, this is rather silly! Much better to do it because you are very much alive! And because it's fun to focus on the stuff you want to do, and get on with it. You know what time it is now don't you? It's Journal o'clock!

Take some quiet time to think about your BUCKET LIST. What are the things you love to do? What makes your heart sing? What makes you feel alive? These questions will help you to decide what to put on your list.

It may include -

Places you want to go

Things you want to experience or learn

Things you would like to achieve

The second thing I love doing is to create a Vision Board. This is a pictorial representation of your ideal life.

Dream big. Huge in fact!

You probably won't know how you are going to achieve this ideal life, or when. But don't let this stop you. Once you get total clarity on what you want, it's amazing how the Universe (or you may think of it as God or whoever you worship) conspires to put things in your path to take you toward your dreams.

Get yourself a huge pile of magazines, scissors, glue – and glitter and stickers if you're feeling creative, and put together your Vision Board. It's huge fun – maybe do it with your partner, or like-minded friend. That's the old-school approach, but it is immensely satisfying. A more up-to-date approach would be to use Pinterest. The choice is yours.

Once you have done this, use the power of your mind and imagination to make it a reality. Many of the techniques described in Chapter 5 work well here. You can visualise your new life – really connect with how it will feel, what will be going on, what people will be saying to you. The more you connect with the life you want for yourself, the more focus you have, and the more you will attract and notice steps which will take you towards your ideal life.

I love to have hopes and dreams, plans and goals for the future. I like my mind, and every single cell in my body to know that I intend to be around for a while yet, to enable me to do all this stuff. It gives a strong message, and expectation, and sets an intention. Powerful stuff.

Life is such an adventure. Cancer is a life-changing part of that adventure. Let's do our utmost to squeeze every bit of enjoyment and fulfilment out of it, and screech noisily and Maverick-like headlong into the future.

Be that short or long, let's truly live it...

nina joy.

If you would like to ask me a question, make a comment on Facebook, leave a book review via email, or sign up for my free newsletter - then go to www.ninajoy.com.

GLOSSARY

Alternative medicine or therapies
This refers to the wide range of practices which have healing effects and are used to improve a patient's health or wellbeing. Treatments are sometimes used instead of conventional medicine, with the intention of treating or curing a health condition.

Bicarbonate of soda
This has a wide range of uses in personal and domestic hygiene. Bicarbonate of soda baths are believed to aid detoxification through the skin.

Budwig diet
Johanna Budwig was a German biochemist who found ways to oxygenate patients and developed a full protocol and diet for cancer patients. http://en.wikipedia.org/wiki/Johanna_Budwig

CAM
Complementary and alternative medicines are treatments that fall outside of mainstream healthcare.

CEA tumour markers
The CEA (carcinoembryonic antigen) is a protein that may appear in the blood of some people with certain kinds of cancers. CEA levels are measured to give an indication of the spread of the disease, or to measure the effectiveness of treatments.

Complementary medicine

This is the term used for treatments used alongside traditional medicine to alleviate the symptoms of a disease, or the side effects of treatments.

CT scan

This stands for 'Computerised Tomography' scan. It takes a series of x-ray pictures of your body from different angles, and gives a series of cross sections of the part of the body being scanned. A computer is used to put the pictures together, which gives a detailed picture of where a tumour is located and how big it is.

Diagnosis

The identification of an illness by examination of the symptoms.

EMF

Electromagnetic fields. Sometimes referred to as EMF pollution. Electromagnetic radiation is emitted from a range of sources such as electrical wiring, electrical appliances, cordless and wireless devices, Wi-Fi and power lines.

Integrative medicine

Combines mainstream (or orthodox) medicine and therapies with CAM therapies which have some high-quality scientific evidence of safety and effectiveness.

Maverick
An unorthodox or independent minded person.

Oncologist
Medical oncologists are physicians trained in the management of cancer. They work in multidisciplinary teams to care for patients from the time of diagnosis through to cure or palliative care. (Source – Royal College of Physicians).

Orthodox medicine
A system in which medical doctors and other healthcare professionals (such as nurses, pharmacists, and therapists) treat symptoms and diseases using drugs, radiation, or surgery. Also called allopathic medicine, biomedicine, conventional medicine, mainstream medicine, and Western medicine. (Source – National Cancer Institute).

Prognosis
An opinion, based on medical experience, of the likely course of a medical condition.

Quark
A type of fresh dairy product, a soft curd cheese, common in the cuisines of German speaking countries.

Systemic chemotherapy
Treatment with chemotherapy drugs that travel through the blood to cells throughout the body, including those not affected by cancer.

T.A.C.E.
This stands for 'transcatheter arterial chemoembolization'. It is a procedure performed to restrict a tumour's blood supply by injecting chemotherapeutic agents into an artery directly supplying a tumour. This ensures the delivery of the chemotherapy in a concentration up to 100 times more than what is achieved systemically. Side effects are minimised because of this.

OODLEBOOKS
Online Book Store

Available from

www.oodlebooks.com and Amazon

both in print and on Kindle.